LIVING
ABOVE
PAIN

Experiencing Joy in
the Midst of Suffering

LIVING
ABOVE
PAIN

ALMA EDITH WELCH

WINEPRESS WP PUBLISHING

ISBN 1-57921-125-9
Library of Congress Catalog Card Number: 98-60796

This book is dedicated to
my physician,
Anthony C. Fouts, M.D.

Contents

~ℳℭ~

Introduction

~~☙~~

God's promise was conditional, but simple when He spoke through Isaiah the powerful words: "they shall mount up with wings like eagles" (Isa. 40:31 TLB).

Stressful moments, unforeseen circumstances, and life-threatening diseases are some of the suffering covered in this book about how to deal with everyday painful situations. Some stouthearted Christians have joined me in proving how to soar serenely like the eagle, regardless of the stormy clouds.

These writings declare the victorious Christian life in the midst of suffering, and they confirm that our strength can be renewed to mount up above turbulent clouds. Much scripture is included, and the powerful key verse is Isaiah 40:31: "But they that wait upon the Lord shall renew their strength. They shall mount up with wings like eagles; they shall run and not be weary; they shall walk and not faint" (TLB).

My local physician's insistence was the catalyst that caused me to pursue the arduous task of writing this book about how I have coped with acute and chronic pain; the encouragement of one of my Mayo Clinic physicians at a later time motivated me further. However, my personal life story covers only a small segment of the fourteen chapters in this book.

In addition to my story, more than twenty-four people have also shared their painful experiences and their triumphs. Together, these varied experiences serve a wide coverage on the subject of pain—emotional, mental, physical, and spiritual.

Living with chronic pain can be understood only by those who experience it, but every human being has pain many times during the day. Shocking? No, not when one realizes that physical suffering is only a small phase of pain, though that is usually what enters our minds when we hear the word "pain." Yet burdens are also painful. A harsh word can cut deeply into an individual's emotions; a sick loved one can weigh heavily on a person's mind; a broken heart, or conflict of any kind, can create pain and sometimes sheer agony. Merely looking into a face seldom reveals the agonizing struggle an individual may be enduring.

I have written this book for all who have, or have had painful experiences, and I hope it will serve as a means for coping with all the complexities of pain.

The contributors explain their experiences, the ramifications of suffering, and how short-term or long-term pain has affected their lives. Notwithstanding, whether the pain be physical, emotional, mental, or spiritual, you will understand the source of the suffering and follow through to the joyful conclusion. The in-depth interpretation of others' painful situations may bring you an understanding of areas previously a mystery.

My years of collecting material on prevalent and severe cases of universal pain led me into an extensive inquiry as to the vastness of human suffering. Countless discussions, interviews, and correspondence with doctors, nurses, other health professionals, and staff members of various organizations, as well as casual acquaintances and dear friends, have been of invaluable help. I give a special thanks for their suggestions and encouragement.

To the outstanding contributors, I also give a heartfelt thanks for enduring anguish as they opened up their real-life experiences and granted permission to share with others their victories. Some have authorized the use of their names and others wish to remain anonymous.

The names and addresses of those who have permitted me to use medical, professional, or statistical information, are listed in the appendix.

Many of the impressive stories may be valuable on such subjects as: abuse, Alzheimer's disease, aneurysm, arthritis, blindness, cancer, death, depression, diabetes, Down's syndrome, drugs, loneliness, Meniere's disease, pet therapy, rape, rebellion, stroke, and suicide.

Throughout the book are pictures of a majestic eagle drawn by an artist friend, Sandy Beard, and the last page (page 190) is a gift for the reader to tear out and frame. We pray that this will be a source of motivation and encouragement to *Living above Pain: Experiencing Joy in the Midst of Suffering.*

Chapter One

Pain Is Universal

⁓𝄞⊙

"The Lord looks from heaven; He see all the sons of men. From the place of His habitation He looks on all the inhabitants of the earth." (Psalm 33:13–14 NKJV)

From the North Pole to the South Pole, encompassing Planet Earth, people are suffering. Millions are injured, or maimed, or killed by crime, accidents, starvation, wars, and nameless atrocities. It is not humanly possible to comprehend the painful happenings occurring every few seconds. As typical human beings, we think such things could never happen to us. However, within the seconds it takes to sit down, or blink an eye, unbelievable tragedies occur. But *God* sees and cares!

The National Safety Council, Itasca, Illinois, gave shocking statistics in their *Accident Facts: 1994 Edition*. It revealed that in the United States alone, every two seconds there is a severe disabling injury from an accident—and a death every six minutes.

This is only a glimpse of the reasons for some of the suffering within the United States; the statistics for the entire world would be monumental. Our focus is frequently on our own national pain, but pain is universal.

An acquaintance of mine witnessed some scenes that he said will never be erased from his memory. In his letter of October 24, 1994, he wrote of the terrible tragedies of Rwanda:

> I went to the Rwandan refugee camps. The refugee center at Goma, Zaire, on the Rwanda border, is in many ways a place of death and hopelessness. It is one of the greatest human tragedies I have ever witnessed. You can not go there without shedding tears . . . a terrible situation . . .
>
> It is a place without hope. You have seen the pictures and heard the statistics of the hundreds of thousands slain in Rwanda. The more than one million Rwandans wandering the countryside around Goma fled and are afraid to go back, but let me tell you about two of the Rwandans I met. One was a wonderful lady who was writing her name, the name of her husband, and the names of her children for anybody who would put a piece of paper in front of her. In that thronging mass of shoulder-to-shoulder humanity, she'd been separated from her family and had no idea where they were. They could be ten miles away or a lifetime away. They could be dead. Yet this woman, sitting in this camp, crying and pleading with people to find her family, had collected around her eight little orphans and was looking after them. She looked like a mother hen with a whole bunch of chicks. My heart went out to that lady. She was unbelievable.
>
> Then I saw a little boy, about twelve years old. I bent down and looked in his face. I don't think he even saw me. His body was there, but his mind was withdrawn into a protective shell. They said he had seen his parents hacked to pieces in front of his eyes. Not just killed, but when their bodies were on the ground they were cut to pieces. And I thought, "Where will this little boy be in another twenty years? What is he going to think about life?" These are the terrible realities of Rwanda.
>
> —*Max Myers, president of Mission Aviation Fellowship*

These terrible tragedies of Rwanda were reported by Max Myers, president of Mission Aviation Fellowship (MAF), an organization that uses planes and electronic communications to meet more than 60,000 critical flight requests each year.

Hope for Hurting People

Medical teams are flown across the borders of needy countries every day. Their mission centers on transportation and communications for missionaries, Christians workers, and local church leaders. The goal is to multiply the effectiveness of the church to save time and lives and extend Christian outreach. Near Rwanda, plans were being laid for sending a medical team across the border to reopen a looted hospital in the southwest part of Rwanda.

The relief work of MAF means lives are saved every day and hurting people are finding hope. The words of Christ compel all servants of Christ, especially this mission with its flying medical teams, to minister to suffering men, women, and children around the world. The war-brutalized people of Rwanda are only the tip of the iceberg. Thank God for our missionaries who are faithfully serving Him in such dangerous places. I am reminded of the Lord's words spoken in one of the Gospels: ". . . whatever you did for one of the least of these brothers of mine, you did for me . . ." (Matt. 25:40 NIV).

News media reports of tragedies around the world become like a broken record. Momentarily our hearts may be touched, then our thoughts go back to ourselves and our own aches and pains.

All of America was in utter dismay, shock, grief, and disbelief when a young mother admitted driving to a lake, jumping out of the car, and sending it rolling into the murky water with her two little boys, fourteen months old and three years old, to their deaths. Then she walked away! As the family, neighbors, friends, acquaintances, strangers, and people all across America listened to the unfolding deplorable, brutal details, our dismay turned to anger and our hearts were overwhelmed with grief and pain. The media reports that at least 50 percent of children murdered today are killed by their own parents. What pain our children suffer because of troubled, demented adults!

Pain is loneliness, rejection, grief, abuse, fear, rape, depression, broken homes, worry, starvation, arthritis, AIDS, back problems, diabetes, cancer, Meniere's disease, stroke . . . any injury, or organic disease. The list goes on and on. Anything that hurts is called pain, whether physical, emotional, spiritual—*any* unpleasant feeling.

These unpleasant feelings relay messages through our complex nervous system to the brain, which interprets and reacts to keep us alive and well. Physical pain is a warning that our body needs attention; our bodies then respond to protect us. David, the psalmist, responds to the marvel of the human body and praises God: "Thank you for making me so wonderfully complex! It is amazing to think about. Your workmanship is marvelous—and how well I know it" (Ps. 139:14 TLB).

Pain *can* be a blessing!

Yes, pain is a blessing many times in our lives, like an SOS calling out for immediate attention. I call it "God's built-in computer" in our bodies.

Pain in the eye can be traumatic, but pain in any part of the body can create a change in one's family's life, demanding undivided attention with no consideration for others or the inconvenience caused by a self-centered reaction. Some people seem to enjoy sympathy so much that they do not deplore any means for obtaining it, even though it may mean hospitalization or surgery. My personal incident of minor eye surgery, and later double vision, was annoying to me and to a brother who had to drive me when I had the eye surgery.

My own reaction then was vanity and distress; vanity because I didn't want anyone to see my eye patch, distress because my brother's spoken embarrassment cut deeply since I was just a young teenager at the time. How minute this incident was! But at the time, it was a painful experience. My thoughts were on myself and my feelings. Isn't that typical of us human beings? I pray that we may look beyond ourselves and think of sufferers who have *no* hope for relief in unreachable, desperate places.

In war-torn and famine-ravaged countries, volunteers report that severe pain is so prevalent that a person's pain may be diminished by concern for those around him and that he may have a higher tolerance for pain than others. The following true story will illustrate these concepts.

Plane Crash in New Guinea

During World War II, a young American Air Force staff sergeant was injured in action in Hollandia, Dutch New Guinea. The news spread quickly about this young man's horrifying experience, his miraculous escape, his personal endurance, courage, and fortitude. He told of his plane crashing in a swampy jungle onto the ground and exploding upon impact. An intense fire engulfed what was left after the crash. Upon regaining consciousness, the sergeant realized he had been catapulted some forty feet into the air, left dangling upside down in a tree, still strapped to the A-20's seat with his armor plate around him. Releasing himself from the seat, he fell to the ground just over a hundred feet from the blazing wreck, landing on his face and head. He attempted to rescue his buddy from the plane, but the intense heat and explosions forced him back, so he struggled through the quagmire in what he hoped was the direction of his base.

He knew God was with him in this dangerous home of cannibal tribes. As God had taken him through that horrible plane crash, he knew that nothing was too hard for his Lord, who had already proved that angels were hovering over him. Alternately staggering and crawling through the dense foliage, he saw a brown haze in the sky and the sound of engines confirmed he was near his base. As he reached the open field, he raised his arms, then collapsed. Later, he rallied enough to realize he was in his squadron's jeep. Then while lying on a cot in the medic's tent with a nurse giving him a shot of morphine, he heard the doctor saying, "His heart is running away!" The doctor told him, "We don't know, Fly Boy, how you got back here."

When he awakened three and a half days later, he had a metal Halloween-like mask over his eyes and nose. Upon seeing himself in a mirror without the mask, he exclaimed: "I look like Jimmy Durante!" After his buddies found a picture of him in his duffel bag, the doctor told him he would break his nose and reshape it as closely as he could to what it once was by using the picture as a model.

The next day, he found himself covered with mosquito netting and lying on a cot in the hospital tent where he spent six days before his release to the United States.

His orders sent him to Shreveport, Louisiana, to the Barksdale Air Force Base where his wife, Rosemary, joined him, and there he served as an instructor on the huge B-20 four-engine super bomber. Included in his orders were instructions regarding a retreat awards ceremony in his honor where a formal presentation of air medals was made to commemorate his bravery in the Pacific Islands. The ceremony was a "welcome back to the good, old USA!"

The Air Force newspaper in Shreveport, *The Barksdale Bark*, carried an illustrated story of this phenomenal young man and his miraculous escape. Louis M. Centobene submitted the following pictures with his permission for printing them along with his story.

Men of Barksdale

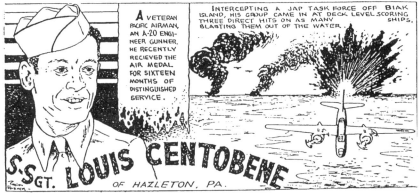

G. Preston Hatcher

CENTOBENE MIRACULOUSLY ESCAPED DEATH WHEN HIS A-20, CARRYING A FULL BOMB LOAD, CRASHED INTO JUNGLES, SETTING THE WHOLE AREA AFIRE. SCOOTING OUT OF THE TURRET, BROKEN AND BLEEDING, THE SWARTHY SERGEANT FLED THROUGH THE FLAMING CRASH PATH TO SAFETY BEFORE THE PLANE'S BOMBS EXPLODED. LESS THAN TWENTY-FOUR HOURS LATER, THE WOUNDED GUNNER STAGGERED BACK TO HIS BASE AT HOLLANDIA, DUTCH NEW GUINEA, FOR MEDICAL TREATMENT. HE WAS THE ONLY SURVIVOR OF THE CREW.

He looked back on those days in the jungle of New Guinea and commented: "The Lord had His hand on me. He made me and gave me the inborn ability and strength to live through that ordeal. I continue to see Him taking care of me every day, wherever I am."

What a joy and comfort to know that wherever we are—anywhere in the universe—God will be with us. He comforts, guides, and rules all circumstances. Whether we are in a war-torn country, a casualty of violent abuse, or the victim of a plane crash, we are in a world filled with inner turmoil. It is a beautiful world; some inhabitants make it a corrupt and painful dwelling place, but God makes *all* things beautiful with our help as His instruments.

Resentment Reigns within the Heart of Fellow Man

Let's look at another kind of universal pain—the coveting for something that belongs to others, which may develop into jealousy, embitterment, and hostility.

I think of King Saul's jealousy of young, handsome David, who was a shepherd boy, but dauntless and quick to acknowledge the Lord's power. He was ridiculed by Goliath, and his life was constantly threatened by King Saul, but David's trust was in the Lord.

Throughout the universe, man habitually resents his fellow man. This resentment frequently builds into a malicious reaction. I have endured this suffering, and the following two experiences emphasize this demoralizing pain.

A family of four visited me while on furlough in the States from Quito, Ecuador. Their ministry report was exciting. The Gene Jordan family serves in MAF reaching many needy people, and, for awhile, Gene worked along the rivers in Ecuador's western jungles. He is a pilot and has played a vital part in helping the suffering by transporting supplies, medical teams, and patients needing hospital care. As of this writing, Gene is regional director for Latin America, serving out of Quito and in nine countries of South and Central America, including Brazil and Haiti. It broke my heart to receive a letter from Gene with the following: "My most painful experience: being falsely accused by a co-worker of actions and decisions he attributed to me. But in reality, I had very little part in it. Lies hurt pretty bad, and it took a long time to work through the problem to where we came to the point that the rest of the staff realized that what had been said had, indeed, been said untruthfully and out of jealousy."

From Ecuador, India, the United States, indeed, anywhere in the world, we hear similar stories. In our Christian organizations, Christian television ministries, local churches, and charities, the problems are overwhelming. The big "I" often gets in the way of a could-have-been-flourishing ministry. When self is in control, other lives can be damaged and sometimes destroyed. But for the devout, Christian person who is hurt, God is always in control, and the all-powerful One turns the evil into good.

Demoralizing Pain in the United States

For fifty years, I have had the joy of knowing a humble, fully surrendered lady whose one purpose in serving the Lord was to be a servant to others. Her unselfish, strong faith and total dedication are unmatched in my experience. I shall purposely enumerate the webbing of this vicious attack against my friend to emphasize the progressive entanglement of devious plots that are too often common today. This friend, Neva Jones Thompson, spent over twenty years as a nurse-midwife in a poverty stricken area of India. She worked with women who had never before had any medical help during pregnancy and delivery. These women and Neva endured many hardships, some unthinkable to American women.

Upon her return to the States, she continued to work as a midwife and to witness for Jesus. It was here in the United States that she had a most painful experience. After working for some time in Georgia, she felt that she was being pushed out of the group of obstetricians and midwives she worked with, instead of them all working together to offer good maternity services. Problems deepened, but she felt she could discuss this with no one. Everyone became "too busy" for the regular weekly staff meetings, and the usual student evaluation meeting was changed to a written statement by the staff and submitted to a certain staff nurse-midwife. The confusing happenings worsened.

A few days later, the staff nurse-midwife called Neva and said her evaluation was upsetting and that since she did not show any ability to monitor students, she should no longer have any contact with them. Neva was stunned, but she performed her duties cheerfully while crying inside. She felt this was the "handwriting on the wall" for her to consider a job elsewhere or retirement. She made a decision to talk to the doctor in charge, only to find out that he was on vacation. So she turned to some good friends and prayer partners at church.

Believing that God had some special purpose, they prayed together for His wisdom and guidance and committed the situation to the Lord.

When the doctor returned from his vacation, he noticed that there was no student to help Neva care for a woman in labor. Upon asking a student why she was not working with Neva, she answered that the staff nurse-midwife had told her not to work with Neva. The doctor changed that instruction and ordered the student to work with her.

It was then that Neva learned that the students had heard some untrue statements, including the rumor that she did not like working with them. It seemed there was too much confusion, and she knew that "God is not the author of confusion" (1 Cor. 14:33a KJV). Her love for the work and the patients, and her trust in God for strength and guidance, kept her going. But that same day, she approached the doctor in his office to tell him that she thought it was time to seek another job. His shocking answer was, "That's fine. We can arrange for you to go as soon as you finish on Sunday." No usual month's notice, no discussion. It seemed important to her to be silent and not to make any statement that might appear critical, but just commit the whole experience to the Lord.

Neva reflected: "As time goes by, we can see more and more that God does control the circumstances of our lives. We need to say, 'What would the Lord teach me?' It does not help to ask why, because He knows what is best, even though we cannot understand that He makes no mistakes. During that whole experience, I was sustained by the fact of God's sovereignty. I claimed His promises in Psalm 37:5: 'Commit everything you do to the Lord. Trust him to help you do it and he will'; verse 7: 'Rest in the Lord; wait patiently for him to act. Don't be envious of evil men who prosper'; and verse 23: 'The steps of good men are directed by the Lord. He delights in each step they take. If they fall it isn't fatal, for the Lord holds them with his hand'" (TLB).

Prayer Changes Things—and People, Too!

Neva's solution to her situation is summed up in her words: "I prayed constantly that He would help me react in the right way. This is a testimony to God's faithfulness and to His sovereignty in my life. He has blessed me more abundantly than I could ever dream. Since that time in Georgia, I have moved to Florida, where He has given me assurance of His care and direction and has given me a wonderful, loving Christian husband. Praise His name. He is all-sufficient! He is ever-present!"

Those who give their lives to help others may themselves be placed in a position to suffer emotionally, mentally, physically, and even spiritually because of people problems. Some of these accentuating circumstances may be brought on by clashing personalities, jealousy, false accusations, and a lying or poisonous tongue.

In some countries, such things may lead to murder, as often happens in political uprisings, or closer to home in uncomfortable domestic situations. I feel the following verses from the third chapter of James are appropriate:

> If any one can control his tongue, it proves that he has perfect control over himself in every other way (vs 2). . . . So also the tongue is a small thing, but what enormous damage it can do. A great forest can be set on fire by one tiny spark. And the tongue is a flame of fire. It is full of wickedness, and poisons every part of the body. And the tongue is set on fire by hell itself, and can turn our whole lives into a blazing flame of destruction and disaster (vss 5–6). Men have trained, or can train, every kind of animal or bird that lives and every kind of reptile and fish, but no human being can tame the tongue. It is always ready to pour out its deadly poison (vss 7–8). . . . For jealousy and selfishness are not God's kind of wisdom. Such things are earthly, unspiritual, inspired by the devil. For wherever there is jealousy or selfish ambition, there will be disorder and every other kind of evil. But the wisdom that comes from heaven is first of all pure and full of quiet gentleness. . . . (vss 15–17*a* TLB)

Looking upon people in painful situations brought on by others, I am thankful we have a God who is compassionate, forgiving, and merciful. "The Lord is gracious and compassionate, slow to anger and rich in love" (Ps. 145:8 NIV).

Modern technology has brought all peoples of Planet Earth closer together. Nothing happens today that the news media does not give special reports. Many times on TV, we see live pictures of torturous events in a city or a country, and we know of universal suffering. The apostle Paul knew the physical, emotional, and mental sufferings from false accusations, imprisonment, beatings, shipwrecks, stonings, robberies, and the many sufferings that he recorded in 2 Corinthians 11:23–28. What a powerful message he has given us in his words from Corinth, a city of Greece: "I am filled with comfort. I am exceedingly joyful in all our tribulation" (2 Corinthians 7:4*b* NKJV).

No one but the person enduring the anguish knows the inner turmoil, and he cries for help and love. The world includes everyone. But God is *no* respecter of persons. He is an all-loving God for people of all walks of life, regardless of where we live. We cannot fathom His love, but His love reaches to the deepest sea. The human being's mind is too finite to comprehend the width, length, depth, and height of the love of Christ, but that doesn't change the fact that Christ loves *all* the children of the world. He alone can soothe the aching heart and painful body as we cry out to Him from anywhere within the universe.

Praise God for such a loving, caring Savior!

"My sheep listen to My voice, I know them, and they follow me." (John 10:27 NIV)

"... no one can snatch them out of my Father's hand." (John 10:29*b* NIV)

Chapter Two

Love Endures Pain

In the beginning, God made man in His own image and said that man should not be alone. So God made him a companion, a woman, to look upon for his delight as a helpmate, to be together always for each other.

Then God spoke through His apostle, Paul, and said, "Husbands, love your wives, just as Christ also loved the church and gave Himself for it" (Eph. 5:25 NKJV).

Within the marriage vows are the words "in sickness and in health . . . till death do us part." But today, only two in five marriages survive. It is a joy to see a husband and wife resolved to establish a Christian home based on the principles in God's Word. Stories of love and pain are in every home, but a home filled with God's love weathers the storms of family life.

Sometimes a serious illness brings out the true love within a spouse's heart, and this chapter is devoted to a very special couple I have known since my college days; they have endured the horrors of Alzheimer's disease. Eugene Michaels, founder of Alzheimer's Disease Research, a program of the American Health Assistance Foundation, says:

No disease known to man can match the heartache and suffering Alzheimer's inflicts on the loved ones of its victims. It is absolutely relentless and ruthless in its assault . . .

It can work quickly and complete its course in two or three years, or it can drag on for as long as twenty torturous years. But the end is always the same—death.

Through it all, it tortures not only its victims, but their families and loved ones as well as they watch its terrible progression in helpless agony.

Alzheimer's disease victims often deteriorate into a childlike, even infantile state, unable to recognize their loved ones, helpless to feed, clothe, or bath themselves, or to even control basic bodily functions. The shocking fact is that every three minutes, Alzheimer's disease claims a new victim, and it kills another American every five minutes. Alzheimer's disease researchers feel they are at crossroads in their battle with what they call "the cruelest disease mankind has ever faced . . . a mind-destroying disease."

There are an estimated four millions victims today in the United States alone. It is heartbreaking to see the Alzheimer's disease victims at nursing homes. However, I am sure it is much more difficult to have this as a moment-by-moment home experience. The person responsible for home care, I believe, is a person with a special heart of inexhaustible love.

I have unforgettable memories of a young couple dating while we were in college. These two were exemplary examples of true love, enduring all phases of a marriage in their everyday lives. Muriel was the daughter of missionary parents and Robertson McQuilkin was the son of the first president of our college, Columbia Bible College, today known as Columbia International University in Columbia, South Carolina. Several years after graduation, Robertson was the headmaster of Ben Lippen School in Asheville, North Carolina, which his father, Dr. Robert C. McQuilkin, had negotiated for in the beginning of his Columbia Bible College presidency. Dr. McQuilkin needed a Bible conference site to continue his powerful Victorious Life Conferences, in addition to his duties at Columbia Bible College.

Mountain of Trust—Ben Lippen

The location of a new conference center on a beautiful mountaintop near Asheville came to fruition; its name was Mountain of Trust and later became known as Ben Lippen, the Scottish rendition of Mountain of Trust. Many years later, Ben Lippen School was moved to Columbia Bible College grounds to become Ben Lippen Schools, kindergarten through twelfth grades.

But Robertson stayed at Ben Lippen, Asheville, for only three years because the Lord had another ministry in Japan for him and his wife, Muriel. This change was a commitment to follow God's direct leading, regardless of where it took him. He had learned that "victory in Christ was the same as taking God at His word." *Victory in Christ* is the title of one of his father's books, and these words were emphatically repeated to Dr. McQuilkin's students at Columbia Bible College and at his many Victorious Life Bible Conferences. As his father, Dr. McQuilkin, used to say, be "definite, concrete, and specific," and he was in his victorious way of teaching and in his lifestyle.

Little did Robertson know the impact the death of the first president of Columbia Bible College, Dr. Robert C. McQuilkin, his father, would have on his life. At age twenty-five, Robertson had been well trained by his dad in the victorious life experience. He had seen many students' lives changed into "a life of victory in Christ," and he was one of those students.

He and Muriel had followed hundreds of other students who accepted God's call into full-time Christian ministry at home and 10,000 miles overseas. Robertson and Muriel served as church-planting missionaries in Japan for twelve years.

Robertson ministered in various countries throughout the years, both to missionary communities and to nationals. They felt their roots were grounded in Japan, and he told several hundred Japanese missionaries that to leave Tokyo would be a "demotion." But only five months later, he had a call to return to the States and become president of Columbia Bible College.

He had told the Japanese missionaries, "If you ever hear that Robertson McQuilkin is leaving Japan, you can be sure of two things: In the first place, you can know that he considers it a *demotion*. In the second place, you can be *sure* that he had a stronger, clearer guidance to leave than he ever had to come." His "stronger, clearer guidance to leave" was confirmed in several ways. Muriel thought they should have a token from Scripture, and there were those, as Robertson expressed.

"I told her it would be so much easier if God could give us a dream as in Bible times. The Japanese believe in dreams. The second night, as I lay on the straw mat floor, for the first time in my life I had a dream that seemed to have an intelligible meaning. For the second time since his death sixteen years earlier, I dreamed about the first president of Columbia Bible College, who was my father, and he was in Tokyo. He was calling me and escorting me through Tokyo International Airport for a flight to Columbia. I awoke and rather remonstrated to the Lord that I had not been serious, and besides, all I could tell from the dream was that my subconscious was apparently not opposed to the thought of revelations. If this was really what the Lord wanted, perhaps He would like to do it again. Toward morning, as I slept again, the dream was repeated! The only conclusive word I received in those days was in line with what God had been teaching me in our work in Japan—that the voice of the church is God's normal way for directing His servants. I would go to the field council and to my Japanese brethren. It was unlikely that they would agree to my leaving Japan. I felt relieved."

Muriel and Robertson felt he was *not* the man Columbia Bible College was looking for. So with Muriel's encouragement, he withdrew to an isolated place for three days, waiting for God to "direct our paths according to His promise."

"God had been speaking to us of how our vertical relationship (our love for Him) must control all other loves, and so we told Him quickly that we would do whatever He desired."

He then stated the reasons why he was *not* the man in his strongly worded "counter application." He outlined why he felt he was *not* the man they were looking for as president. Furthermore, he submitted to them a "clear statement of the basic principles, by which, in his opinion, the work of God in a Bible college in the United States should be operated."

As told in the milestones of history in the book, *Towers Pointing Upward*, by R. Arthur Mathews, Robertson suggested, "If anyone thought to recapture a former era through the calling of a second Robert C. McQuilkin, he would be greatly disappointed."

He further stated, "God only made one Robert C. McQuilkin, and though I could wish it otherwise, my gifts and calling were not his."

Accepted His "Demotion" to Go to Columbia

The college board felt even more convinced that Robertson McQuilkin was God's choice. Finally, Robertson accepted his "demotion" as the will of God, to give himself to Columbia Bible College for the task of leading missionaries and Christian leaders of that generation "To know Him and to make Him known"—the motto of Columbia International University to this day.

Several months later at his inaugural address, Robertson McQuilkin made a profound statement: "Columbia Bible College is known around the world for its teaching on Christlike living. God grant that we may be known not only for the teaching, but for the living." At the end of this address, he said, "As I am commissioned today by the Board of Trustees to be the third president of Columbia Bible College, and as I receive ordination for this ministry from their hands, I pledge myself to stand on the foundation of the Word of God alone, and to give myself wholly to the pursuit of these two goals: that we might become increasingly like Jesus and our students may become increasingly like Jesus; and that we, and they, may become ever more effective in making Him known."

When they lost their thirty-six-year-old son, Robert McQuilkin, who drowned in Lake Michigan in sixty-two feet of water in the Straits of Mackinac while on a Chicago magazine assignment photographing a Lake Michigan shipwreck, they were united in sorrow and comfort for each other. Was this an introduction to a deeper life of sorrow?

Then while on a vacation in Florida, Robertson observed Muriel's repetition of a story to their host that she had just told five minutes earlier. This began to happen occasionally. Then three years later during a hospitalization for her, a doctor said to Robertson, "You may need to think about the possibility of Alzheimer's." Robertson was incredulous, but he saw other indications too. Muriel had many talents, but while painting a portrait of Robertson one day, she encountered uncommon difficulty. The college and seminary board had been impressed by her earlier splendid portrait of his predecessor, Dr. G. Allen Fleece, but now she struggled.

Muriel's memory was deteriorating, so he took her to a neurologist friend, who, through many tests, confirmed that Muriel had Alzheimer's. He was deeply shaken when the doctor asked her to name the gospels, only to see Muriel look at him pleadingly for help. "She laughed at herself," Robertson said. "And she was a little nervous, perhaps, but nothing was going to get her down."

Muriel had a morning radio program called *Looking Up*, which was designed for women, but businessmen often told Robertson "how they arranged their morning affairs so they could catch the program." But one day, the radio station manager asked Robertson for an appointment. He remembers their uneasiness as the appointment began. He wrote in his book, *Living by Vows*:

> After a few false starts, I caught on. Only months before they had talked of national syndication. Now they were reluctantly letting me know that an era was ending. I tried to help them out. "Are you meeting with me to tell us that Muriel cannot continue?" They seemed relieved that their painful message was out and none of them had to say it. So I thought, "Her public ministry is over. No more conferences, TV, radio. I should have guessed the time had come."

Muriel insisted on accepting speaking invitations, but as Robertson wrote:

> She would come home crushed and bewildered that her train of thought was lost and things did not go well. Gradually, reluctantly, she gave up her public ministry.

Some of the pain was eased to know that Muriel never knew what was happening to her, though occasionally when there was reference to Alzheimer's on TV, she would muse aloud, "I wonder if I'll ever have that?" It did not seem painful for her, but it was a slow dying for me to watch the vibrant, creative, articulate person I knew and loved, gradually dimming out.

Robertson approached the college board of trustees with his dilemma and told them that they needed to begin a search for his successor. He knew that Muriel would eventually need him full-time, and he informed the board that she would have him when that day had come. As usual, his friends, "wise and godly," urged him to arrange for institutionalization, but he pondered many thoughts: *Would Muriel become accustomed to the new environment quickly? Would she? Would anyone love her at all, let alone love her as I do?*

I had often seen the empty, listless faces of those lined up in wheelchairs along the corridors of such places, waiting, waiting for the fleeting visit of some loved one. In such an environment, Muriel would be tamed only with drugs or bodily restraints, of that I was confident. People who do not know me well have said, 'Well, you always said, God first, family second, ministry third,' But I never said that! To put God first means that all other responsibilities He gives are first too.

In 1988 we planned our first family reunion since the six children had left home, a week at a mountain retreat. Muriel delighted in her children and grandchildren, and they in her. We planned it as the celebration of our 'fortieth' anniversary, although it was actually the thirty-ninth. We feared that by the fortieth she would no longer know us!

She cannot comprehend much, nor express many thoughts, and those, not for sure. But she knows whom she loves, and she lives in a happy oblivion to almost everything else. She is such a delight to me. I don't *have* to care for her, I *get* to! One blessing is the way she is teaching me so much—about love, and for example, God's love. She picks flowers outside—anyone's—and fills the house with them. Lately, she has begun to pick them inside, too. A friend had given us a beautiful Easter lily, two stems with four or five lilies on each, and more to come. One day I came into the kitchen, and there on the window sill, over the sink, was a vase with a stem of (Easter) lilies in it. The next day, our youngest son, soon to leave for India, came from Houston for his next-to-last visit. As we sat on the porch swing, savoring each moment together, his mother came to the door with a gift of love for me. Then she carefully laid the other stem of lilies on the table with a gentle smile and turned back into the house. Muriel cannot speak in sentences now, only in phrases and words, and often words that make little sense: "no" when she means "yes," for example. But she can say one sentence, and she says it often: "I love you." She not only says it, she acts it!

The board arranged for a companion to stay in our home so I could go daily to the office. During those two years, it became increasingly difficult to keep Muriel home. As soon as I left, she would take out after me. With me, she was content; without me, she was distressed, sometimes terror stricken. The walk to school is a mile roundtrip. She would make that trip as many as ten times a day. Sometimes at night when I helped her undress, I found bloody feet. When I told our family doctor, he choked up. "Such love," he said simply. Then after a moment, "I have a theory that the characteristics developed across the years come out at times like these." I wish I loved God like that—desperate to be near Him at all times. Thus, she teaches me day by day.

I have a long list of "coping strategies," which have to be changed weekly, sometimes daily. Grocery shopping together may have been recreation, but it is not so much fun when Muriel begins to load other people's carts and takes off with them, disappearing into the labyrinth of supermarket aisles. Or, how do you get a person to eat or take a bath when she steadfastly refuses? . . .

As she needed more and more of me, I wrestled daily with the question of who gets me full time—Muriel or Columbia? When the time came, the decision was firm. It took no great calculation. It was a matter of integrity. Had I not promised forty-two years before, "in sickness and in health . . . till death do us part?"

She had, after all, cared for me for almost four decades with marvelous devotion, and now it was my turn. And such a partner she was! If I took care of her for forty years, I would never be out of her debt. But how could I walk away from the responsibility of a ministry God had blessed so remarkably during our twenty-two years at Columbia Bible College and Seminary? Resignation was painful; but the right path was not difficult to discern.

No, it was not a choice between two loves. Both loves—for Muriel and for Columbia Bible College and Seminary—dictated the same choice. There was no conflict of loves then, or of obligations. I have been startled by the response to the announcement of my resignation. Husbands and wives renew marriage vows, pastors tell the story to their congregations. It was a mystery to me until a distinguished oncologist who lives constantly with dying people told me, "Almost all women stand by their men; very few men stand by their women."

It is all more than keeping promises and being fair, however. As I watch her brave descent into oblivion, Muriel is the joy of my life. Daily, I discern new manifestations of the kind of person she is, the wife I always loved. I also see fresh manifestations of God's love—the God I long to love more fully.

Dr. Robertson McQuilkin's story of his struggle first appeared in *Christianity Today*, at the request of their editors. He said in a "McQuilkin Update" in the Columbia International University Quarterly, Spring 1994: "I am constantly amazed at the reprint activity on 'Living by Vows'—at least one magazine a month, three years after its original publications! So the Lord continues to enable me to minister as a homemaker, speaker, and writer—three activities I greatly enjoy!"

In his letter to me February 1, 1995, Robertson wrote:

> Muriel, a little over a year ago, lost her ability to stand or walk and also to feed herself. Although, even today, she reached out, grabbed a glass of juice, and took a drink. This is startling, for it has not happened in many months. She is very content and cheerful. She usually smiles at me two or three times a day—and I live for that! It is no burden to care for her, she is so lovable.

He is a devoted father, as well as husband. In his 1994 Christmas letter, he wrote: "My children bring me great joy. Yet, do you choose love? *Then* you choose pain. And each of them in his and her own way challenges me to 'fly closer to the flame.'"

Dr. Robertson McQuilkin's story is a living example of the love chapter in the Bible, as follows:

> Love is very patient and kind, never jealous or envious, never boastful or proud, never haughty or selfish or rude. Love does not demand its own way. It is not irritable or touchy. It does not hold grudges and will hardly even notice when others do it wrong. It is never glad about injustice, but rejoices whenever truth wins out. If you love someone you will be loyal to him no matter what the cost. . . . All the special gifts and powers from God will someday come to an end, but love goes on forever (1 Cor. 13:4–8a TLB).

The love of God has reached many lives through this day-by-day, ongoing story of Robertson's love for his wife. Can we really comprehend the anguish he has been going through for many years because of the "torturous years" of watching his beloved wife deteriorate into such an unbelievable condition? How many spouses would endure this hardship? Do you really choose to love a spouse "in sickness and in health"? Then, you *will* choose pain!

Robertson's faithfulness and loyalty in fulfilling his promise to love and cherish Muriel in all circumstances is like a beacon proclaiming to others—*love endures pain*—regardless of the cost. But only the love of Jesus Christ makes this love possible.

Chapter Three

Agony of Rebellion

⤙✤☉

". . . rebellion is like the sin of divination, and arrogance like the evil of idolatry." (1 Samuel 15:23*a* NIV)

A rebellious person has a long list of characteristics: seditious, disorderly, unruly, insubordinate, disobedient, incorrigible, defiant, radical, and just simply unhappy. But they are not really aware of their problem. To their loved ones, especially the mother, rebellion brings *much* pain. A mother's heart is broken many times by such a child, but it can usually be mended by three powerful words: I love you!

Years pass and these words are heard less frequently in our homes. A mother's loving care for her baby through many sleepless nights and countless crisis situations are soon forgotten when the child reaches the teenage years. The rebellion of adolescence surfaces when the child is struggling with feelings, either inferiority or superiority. But the attitude the parent sees most often is that "parents just don't understand." There is a dislike for any discipline, especially from anyone in a "parent" category. Mostly, they have a need for love and attention but want it on terms that are satisfactory to them. Their justification is "I live in the nineties—everybody does it." Now, the "it" can refer to many things, depending on just what the child wants to categorize and rationalize in order to do "their thing." But all adults are considered "out of touch."

The reason there is such rebellion, misery, and unhappiness is summed up in the following statement spoken by St. Augustine of Hippo: "Our hearts were made for you, O Lord, and they are restless until they rest in you."

When God spoke to Jeremiah about the people of Judah, He said, "'But this people has a defiant and rebellious heart; they have revolted and departed. . . . Shall I not punish them for these things? . . .'" (Jer. 5:23, 29*a* NKJV). Calamity and pain come with rebellious ways, but repentance and acceptance of Jesus as Savior give rest, peace, and eternal hope for our souls.

A Typical Story of a Rebellious Daughter

One of the most humble and sweetest persons I have known has written about her spiritual triumph over the pain she suffered through years with a rebellious teenage daughter. She is now living in another country, thousands of miles from the United States, but she opened her heart to me in the following story:

> My two youngest daughters were my pride and joy. They were responsible, truthful, and received excellent grades in school. They were members of the National Honor Society in the States. However, one fact bothered me. One of the girls attracted undesirable boys. My concerns were confirmed when I read Proverbs 27:19: "A mirror reflects a man's face, but what he is really like is shown by the kind of friends he chooses" (TLB).
>
> One October, both girls made a commitment to Christ. The girl who attracted problem boys started reading her Bible, going on in her faith and in a friendship with two boys, one totally undesirable. Should I attempt to cut off her new friendships? Seeing her progress in the Lord, I bit my lip and kept quiet. But in February, the questionable boy decided he wanted a more serious relationship with my daughter. My husband and I warned against it. Once when she suggested a breakup, he became abusive and he *dragged* her across a soccer field! We pointed out that he was

undisciplined, but she kept going back to him. She seemed as firmly addicted to him as to a drug. An angry wall of silence was erected between us. He bought identical rings for them and continued to win her affections. She told me later that she was planning to change her last name. I asked advise of everyone—teachers, friends, dorm parents, pastors, counselors. I read everything I could and filed away any appropriate piece of wisdom, but knew if I mentioned it, it would fall on deaf ears.

The girls went to college. I remember inadvertently seeing my daughter's phone bill. It was $360 for one month, and we were scrimping to send her to college! Any money she earned in the student work programs went to pay for phone calls to her out-of-town boyfriend! I tried to be patient and wait on God. "The wheels of God grind slowly, but they grind exceedingly fine!"

A pastor finally counseled me: "Give her a choice—her boyfriend or her education. You don't owe her a college education." With a sad heart, I followed his advice—and she left home.

After leaving home, she found work in a Christian organization. At her Christian workplace, my daughter made some alarming discoveries: One of her friends turned out to be lesbian, and another had a husband who beat her. Yet another had been divorced by her husband because she had committed adultery. My daughter looked again at her family and decided we weren't so bad after all!

In order to keep up her education, she enrolled in night school in a secular college for a course in philosophy. When I heard about this, I wrung my hands. "Now she will leave the faith!" I moaned. But that was a turning point. When the professor asked contemptuously, "Who believes in Creation?", she felt it was now or never. She raised her hand and stated her conviction. Afterward, a classmate congratulated her on her stand and confided, "I'm a Christian too." She thought to herself, "Where were you when I needed support?"

On the final exam, the same type of question was asked. My daughter wrote her Christian conviction, knowing she might receive a lower grade. However, she received an "A" anyway.

Another thing took place. My daughter was attending a certain church and suddenly the pastor preached for three weeks on obedience. My daughter later recalled being so angry at the sermon that she nearly stood up in church and shouted at the pastor. Sunday noon, when she returned from church, she was in a very bad mood and asked herself, "Why am I so angry?" She finally admitted that some aspects of her relationship with the boyfriend did not reflect obedience. She decided to send him a "talking cassette," telling him her feelings. His cassette response: "Glad to hear you want to break up. I was wanting to break up anyway." She was devastated.

Over the next several months, she tried to call him three times but could never get through. She said it must have been the Lord. Then the long slow process of healing began. She had been on prescription drugs for suicidal impulses and now asked to be slowly taken off. She experienced new peace. She went back to the Christian college and graduated with a master of arts in missions.

And I grew more than she did. I looked at myself and started working on my own life instead of hers. A counselor once said to me, "We have never had a teenager cured until the parent changes first." I was forced to accept responsibility for my contribution to our troubled relationship, and I grew spiritually; I also had to learn the meaning of "in His time."

The psalmist said: "Commit thy way unto the Lord; trust also in him, and he shall bring it to pass" (Ps. 37:5 KJV). I learned that patience had an ultimate reward. My greatest pain became a spiritual triumph!

—Anonymous mother, somewhere in Asia

While the foregoing was written about a mother's rebellious teenager, the following heart-rending story is related by a young mother about her own rebellion, which went beyond her teenage years. This mother requested that she be called by the pseudonym, "Holly." She has painfully availed her years as a rebellious teenager.

Holly: A Rebellious Teen

For ten years, she said she went from man to man, and thought for many years that sex was love. It began at age thirteen when she was introduced to sex and drugs. When she had spent the night with a friend about age thirteen, her friend's dad said she could sleep in his bed. After she went to bed, the man got into the bed with her and started hugging and kissing her, then had sexual intercourse with her. She says she didn't think it was wrong at the time and later realized that worldly people like this man may take advantage of an innocent child. Then she said, "That gave me the idea that night that men would love me if I would have sex with them." She said she looked about twenty at age fifteen and was going out to night clubs to dance, drink, and meet men. She was smoking cigarettes and pot and went deeper into alcohol.

Many of Holly's remarks I shall quote because I believe a high percentage of teenagers today have the same attitude she had at that young age. First she tried writing her story, but couldn't. Then she tearfully told me some incidents until she could coordinate the following:

> Rebelliousness or waywardness tends to come naturally to some teenage girls. I should know; I was one of them! You might be thinking what a terrible person I must have been, but I didn't believe that. I thought that I was just like any other girl wanting a man to love her completely. Even though I was partying a lot, *I was very lonely*.
>
> I can remember a time when I was so lonely, I just went to a corner of a room, sat down, and cried because I thought that no one loved me. My heart was breaking, and no one seemed to care. My sister tried to talk to me, but I felt like she was from another planet, so I did not listen to what she tried to say. She was one of several people in my life who led me down the wrong road. When I was twelve or thirteen years old, my sister and her friend introduced me to pot. They finally got tired of hiding it from me, so they let me smoke part of a joint. I never got addicted to it.
>
> I grew up in the shadow of my older brother; I used to think that I could, and should, do everything he did. In the process, I hurt my mother very deeply! My brother used to drink and do drugs, so I did too! He led a promiscuous life, so I did too! I wanted to be so much like my brother; it just didn't matter what I did.

In spite of her wayward life, she went to school and finished high school. She did not know, nor did she care, whether her mother knew what she was doing.

Her first pregnancy came at age nineteen when she was making an effort to attend college. She did not know until she was eleven weeks pregnant, and she chose to have the pregnancy terminated at twelve weeks.

At age twenty-two, with an older man, she had a second pregnancy. That story she recounted:

> That relationship went on for about four or five months, and the night he left town was the night that I got pregnant. It got to the point that he did not call me or anything. I did not know what to do, because I did not want to trap him into marrying me. I decided to terminate my pregnancy again. I had had problems the first time, because I cramped so much and bled a lot afterwards.
>
> I was with Mother, but she did *not* know that I had been pregnant, *nor* that I had had an abortion. You have to have money to have an abortion. I worked to make the money and borrowed some from a friend. I went to a women's clinic. Someone had to take me to the clinic, so they could drive me home afterwards. All they gave me was medication for relaxation. My second pregnancy was terminated, and I did not have any complications. I never had any regrets about the abortions, for *I felt it was not a baby; it was merely fetal tissue*, and I thought nothing was wrong about it. I said it was my body, and I had my own choice. I did not consult anybody, but people did tell me it was wrong. I did not believe them, nor did I want to believe them.
>
> My mother loved me in her own special way. She took care of my basic needs in life: food, clothes, and shelter, and I took it all for granted. I treated her disrespectfully because I was wrapped up in my secret life. I was the baby of my family, and by the time I became a teenager, her daddy needed extra care. She worked full-time as a nurse, and after work, she traveled about twenty miles to take care of him. She arrived home about seven or eight o'clock every night, so she did not have a life to herself, nor did she have much time for me. My mother was, and is, a very wonderful person.

I know that it was by my mother's prayers and God's grace that I am alive today! My daddy died when I was fourteen, so I was my mother's sole responsibility, yet I did not appreciate her. She struggled to take care of me and her father at the same time. I grew up not knowing what love from a real daddy was like. I had wanted so much more than anything for my daddy to love me when he was alive, but he didn't! He had a greater love—a bottle of whiskey.

But *God* loved me. He directed me to a man whom I really loved. We married, and I thought I would be the happiest girl for the rest of my life. I was for the first six months, then our marriage went "on the rocks." We thought about divorce, but during that time, I became pregnant. It was then that I realized that I was responsible for another life. We knew we had to make our marriage work because of the child I was carrying. My husband looked at me in a whole new light, realizing it was his child.

Our attitude toward each other changed. I started having a desire to go to church. After I had the baby, the desire did not go away. I visited a church, and the pastor and his wife came to visit my husband and me. That night they shared the gospel of Christ with us. They asked us two questions: "If you were to die tonight, where would you spend eternity?" and "If you were to die tonight and stand before God, and He were to ask you, 'Why should I let you into my heaven?' what would you say?"

My husband and I both knew we were not perfect, but we knew that we were good people by the world's standards. Then the pastor told us that God had a free gift that He wanted to offer us—and it was the gift of salvation. All we had to do was to believe on the Lord Jesus and we would be saved, ". . . that if you confess with your mouth Jesus as Lord, and believe in your heart that God raised Him from the dead, you shall be saved" (Rom. 10:9–10 NASB).

That night my husband and I accepted Jesus Christ as our Lord and Savior. It was a whole new beginning for us! As we started growing in Christ, Satan brought back my past life to haunt me, but nothing was more devastating than the memories of taking the lives of my two unborn children. I went through months of agony because Satan had me believing that God could forgive all my sins except the abortions. It took God's Word, and a faithful servant of His, to show me that God had already forgiven me and that it was time for me to forgive myself. "If we confess our sins, He is faithful and righteous to forgive us our sins and to cleanse us from all unrighteousness" (1 John 1:9 NASB).

Soon after that, the bondage was no longer there. I felt like a new person in Christ and did not hurt inside any more. I am a born-again Christian because Jesus Christ is Lord of my life. I recently celebrated my fifth "birthday" as a new creature in Christ. Praise God for 2 Corinthians 5:17, which says "When someone becomes a Christian he becomes a brand new person inside. He is not the same any more. A new life has begun!" (TLB). It took time for Jesus to heal all those painful wounds, but He did, one by one. He is now using me to help other women heal from the bondage that ties them down.

"We are Christ's ambassadors. God is using us to speak to you. . . ." (2 Cor. 5:20a TLB).

—*"Holly," Dixieland*

God's command is to repent for rebellious ways. God told Ezekiel to tell the house of Israel, "'This is what the Sovereign Lord says: Repent! Turn from your idols and renounce all of your detestable practices!" (Ezek. 14:6b NIV). Idols are anything that take precedence over the Lord, and today, drugs, sex, alcohol, and possessions are some of the idols in our lives. The Bible has documented the sufferings endured by the Israelites who consistently rebelled against God; consequently they endured great hardships and even death.

Again, I refer to King Saul whose rebellious ways are recorded in 1 Samuel 15:1–30. He *disobeyed* the word of the Lord and did what he wanted to do. He was arrogant, self-centered, and was more interested in pleasing people than the One who had permitted him to be king. King Saul proved to be a liar and a defiant, fickle king. Therefore, the prophet Samuel boldly told King Saul that the Lord had given his kingdom to one better than he.

He suffered the consequence of his arrogant life. What could be more devastating and painful than being removed from the highest position in one's country?

God is all-knowing and looks beyond our outward appearance into our hearts. When the Lord had Samuel anoint David to replace King Saul, God said to Samuel, "Do not consider his appearance or his height, for I have rejected him. The Lord does not look at the things man looks at. Man looks at the outward appearance, but the Lord looks at the heart" (1 Sam. 16:7 NIV).

People who refuse to subject themselves to higher authority, such as parents, officers, and kings, are not capable to accept responsibility. Paul, an apostle of Jesus Christ, told Titus in his epistle, "Remind the people to be subject to rulers and authorities, to be obedient, . . . to show humility toward all men" (Titus 3:1–2 NIV).

When we repent and ask forgiveness for our disobedient acts and then totally submit to the love and saving grace of Jesus Christ, our changed lives become a joy to ourselves and others. Our old miserable lives take a new meaning to fulfilling the purpose for which God created us in glorifying the Sovereign Lord.

"The Lord is my Shepherd, I shall not want." (Ps. 23:1)

"Thy rod and Thy staff, they comfort me." (Ps. 23:4*b*)

Chapter Four

Childhood Abuse

—— ✤ ——

"The neglect and abuse of children is one of American's greatest problems. There were 3.1 million recorded incidents last year. A child was abused every thirteen seconds and four died each day."
—CHILDHELP USA: Woodland Hills, California

Startling statistics! I was amazed at the informative data of CHILDHELP USA. For thirty-six years, the organization has "refined its services to abused children, their families, and teenage and adult survivors of childhood abuse."

One paragraph in its letter of April 15, 1995, further stated: "Child abuse happens on all income, social, and educational levels, and among all races and religions. But it is more common when children live in poverty, with an unmarried or divorced parent, or in an environment where people are abusing alcohol or drugs."

However, in today's environment, the abusive acts of alcohol and sodomy reach *all* ages in *all* walks of life. Why are sodomy and perverted ways so prevalent today? Looking at the Old Testament days, when the children of Israel had no strong leaders, they willingly followed the negative influence. The book of Judges records an example of the wickedness of corrupt men who did "what was right in their own eyes." They demanded a sojourner to a man's home to come out to them so "that we may know him carnally"!

When they couldn't get this visitor, they took his wife and "abused her all night until morning"; in fact, they abused her to death (Judg. 19:22–28 NKJV). These were adults, but they lived in a city similar to Sodom, thus the word "sodomy".

These men in Gibeah had an environment that marred their lives, but they were punished by the children of Israel according to their command: "Now therefore, deliver up the men, the perverted men who are in Gibeah, that we may put them to death and remove the evil from Israel!" (Judg. 20:13*a* NKJV).

In Biblical days, sin was removed from the people according to the law of Moses; if this was not performed as God had commanded Moses, then they would receive punishment directly from God. The punishment could be upon the entire city as it was upon Sodom, thus the children of Israel obeyed God and fulfilled His punishment for these men from Gibeah. Where is our nation's consistency in handling wrongdoing today? Where are our Christian leaders to enforce our laws?

The above Biblical story dealt with adults, but we shall mention only two abusive acts to children, similar, and maybe identical, to those that are occurring each day. From California, a friend, Evelyn Williams, recounted the following abuse story to be used solely for this book. It aptly portrays the demoralizing environment conducive to abuse and the action she took that honored God by taking a child from a degenerate life.

From Neglect to Victory

Evelyn's story began in the summer of 1975 when she was pregnant and had met a neighbor six months pregnant, who was an alcoholic. Evelyn had a miscarriage two months after her friend's baby was born. Only one day after her loss, her neighbor asked Evelyn if she would keep her baby because she was "too nervous" to care for him. It was obvious she had been drinking heavily, but Evelyn told her that she was too weak from her miscarriage. So the mother staggered away holding her baby. The following week the baby boy was taken from his mother and placed in a foster home.

But the woman came back to Evelyn begging her to get her baby and take care of him until she "recovered." The mother kept pleading for the social worker to return her baby and made promises that she would stop drinking. The mother then moved to a Los Angeles ghetto, and finally she was given another chance when the boy was seven years old. But, the little boy wandered the streets, begging for food; many times he tried to get his own food as his mother lay drunk on the bed or on the floor. He seldom attended school, lived in dirty clothes, and rarely had a bath.

One day, Evelyn went by their apartment and found cigarette burns under his neck. She called the police and then took the case to court where she agreed to accept legal guardianship. Evelyn continued the story:

> During the years in our home, we, as a family of four, have loved and accepted Jayson as our own son. He adjusted well in his new home, and throughout his public school years, he had an excellent attendance record.
>
> Jayson has been a joy to me and my family. He became a speaker and youth leader in his church activities and did extremely well in speaking and singing.
>
> In his early teens, he was elected by our church as a speaker to represent the youth at the Martin Luther King Celebration in Los Angeles. Then he was sent as one of our church's messengers to the National Baptist Convention in Detroit. At age sixteen, he was sent by our church to the state convention in Palms Springs. Later, he and another youth went with our pastor to a national convention in Detroit to interact with youths from around the United States. He sang with the Pasadena Youth Choir for several years and was given second place in our church's oratorical contest. He also spoke at layman breakfasts in different Pasadena and Los Angeles churches. He delighted in working with the laymen in feeding the homeless.
>
> We have not pushed him, but we have helped him with our advice and have been proud of his choices. He still remembers the times when he was living in the ghetto, the times he tried to

awaken his mother to feed him or give him a bath, and also remembers neighbors feeding him and then complaining about taking care of him. I am thankful that he is not bitter, nor resentful of his mother.

If it had not been for the strength of the Lord, I could not have gone through those early years. I prayed for wisdom and guidance, and God worked everything out in such a beautiful way for this fine young man. Jayson makes friends easily and has amazed us in his decisions and accomplishments. We are thankful for his beautiful life because he loves the Lord and wants his life to count for Him. As of this writing, he is twenty-one and is serving his country in the Air Force.

We are so proud of him! Surely, nothing is too hard for God! We have just trusted and leaned on Him for everything. I have seen God's promise in Proverbs 3:5–6 fulfilled: "Trust in the Lord

Jayson Phelps

with all your heart, And lean not on your own understanding; In all your ways acknowledge Him, And He shall direct your paths" (NKJV).

I know Jayson is in His hands now, and I expect a great future for him.

—*Evelyn Williams, Pasadena, California*

Thanks to Evelyn and her family for the influence they have had upon this young man. The impact of a loving family has proved the powerful, life-changing influence that good moral values have made upon a life. This young man had a sad, abusive infancy and early childhood. Because his environment was changed to a loving, Christian, churchgoing family, he had a chance to blossom into a strong, wholesome individual. Prayer *does* change conditions and people!

Girl Molested by Brothers

Another abuse story was written by a lady in Pennsylvania with the strong request not to disclose her name. She wishes to be called "Ann." Her sad story was hidden for years, and she thought that she had blocked all remembrances out of her mind. She believed the media reports of so many incest cases brought her nightmares to the surface. Therefore, she realized she was not alone and offered to share the following with the prayer that others may be helped.

When Ann was about eight or nine years of age, she was still sleeping in the same bed with two older brothers. She opened her heart for this book to warn parents that their children *will* experiment and that youngsters should *not* be permitted to sleep together at any age, more so in this day of exposure to so much immoral sex and violence and the breakdown of moral values.

The first time her oldest brother touched her body, he told her it was natural to do. He pretended to be a big brother who needed to teach his little sister what she should know. He said he could make her feel "real good." Then he raped her. She was angry and frightened! Her brother told her not to tell their mother that he had taught her the "secret of life." He warned that their mother would get upset because, he said, she would want to tell her daughter about "nature."

Shortly thereafter, she was alone in the bed with another brother who also raped her. She felt those two brothers had discussed it, because they both said the same thing about their mother. But one day, while alone with the oldest brother, he pushed her to the floor and raped her a second time. She fought and told him to never touch her again. He became angry and threatened her if she told their mother anything about what had happened. She lived in fear not knowing what he might do to her.

Within eight months of the last experience, her menstrual period began. Ann was horrified! No one had ever mentioned anything to her about menstrual periods. She felt something terrible had happened to her. She hid her soiled underwear because she was afraid to tell her mother. She felt that her brothers had caused this to happen. But it didn't take long for her mother to discover her panties. Ann cried and asked what had happened to her. Only then did her mother seem concerned because Ann had just turned eleven years old. She had unbearable pain, later combined with migraines, during each monthly period. Each month, she relived what her brothers had done for their own satisfaction. In fact, she wanted to be alone, away from everyone, as she felt no one cared, and she had no one with whom to discuss her inner suffering.

At an early age, she began having excessive bleeding each month, and the doctor confirmed that she had a serious problem and should be hospitalized. She refused.

Soon extreme weakness prevented her returning to the doctor's office, so he went to their residence and told them that surgery was urgent to save her life. Surgery was ordered shortly after admittance, and she had a complete hysterectomy. She was devastated knowing that she could never have children. Bitterness, resentment, and even hatred, welled up in her. She blamed her mother and wanted to talk with the doctor alone, but her mother was always there. One day Ann began crying and told her mother that she felt she was being punished because of her brothers. She asked her mother why she had permitted them to sleep with her. Her mother never answered. Ann pleaded with her, asking if she really knew what they had done. Her mother only stared, appearing not to hear. Didn't her mother care?

After no response to her insistent pleas, Ann felt her mother did know, but didn't care, was not regretful, sorry, or remorseful. Crying helped Ann, but a great barrier arose between her and her mother. She left home when she got a job and became involved with her work and church, keeping her "secrets" to herself. She wondered if she would ever find a "decent" young man.

One day she found victory over her problems in a scripture verse, and she repeated it over and over: "Cast all your anxiety on Him because He cares for you" (1 Pet. 5:7 NIV). She discovered that God really cared for her, and she knew that only the Lord had gotten her through that painful experience with her brothers and her mother.

To this day, Ann said she has never consulted a human being. She just leaned *totally* on the Lord, crying out to Him to heal her pain—and He did, and He gave her His strength to live above a situation that could have ruined her life. Her mother's reactions hurt deeply, but in spite of a deplorable childhood, living away from her family made her stronger and self-sufficient. She turned her life over to the Lord, and He gave her daily courage, peace, comfort, endurance, and guidance to overcome her painful experience. At her request, I am ending her story with some Bible verses that have helped her.

> Be of good courage, and he shall strengthen your heart, all ye that hope in the Lord. (Ps. 31:24 KJV)

> I love the Lord because he hears my prayers and answers them. Because he bends down and listens, I will pray as long as I breathe! (Ps. 116:1–2 TLB)

> Peace I leave with you; my peace I give you. I do not give to you as the world gives. Do not let your hearts be troubled and do not be afraid. (John 14:27 NIV)

Isn't this similar to the story of Absalom's beautiful sister, Tamar, whose half-brother raped her (2 Sam. 13:1–22)? God condemns the acts of such people strongly in 1 Corinthians 6:9–11a:

> Do you not know that the unrighteous will not inherit the kingdom of God? Do not be deceived. Neither fornicators, nor idolaters, nor adulterers, nor homosexuals, nor sodomites, nor thieves, nor covetous, nor drunkards, nor revilers, nor extortioners will inherit the kingdom of God. And such were some of you. . . . (NKJV)

But our God is a good God, and He wants all who believe on Him to be forgiven. Ann and Evelyn, with Jayson, endured some hard times, but God provided a way, which they found in Him by trusting and obeying His Word. Continuing with the rest of 1 Corinthians 6:11: ". . . but you were washed, but you were sanctified, but you were justified in the name of the Lord Jesus and by the Spirit of our God" (NKJV).

Only the blood of Jesus can wash away our sins.

Nothing in all the world can give that inner joy and peace that "Ann," Evelyn, and Jayson found in Jesus Christ. Jesus is the solution to *every* problem! His grace is sufficient!

"Wait on God; believe; rejoice, and see great things He'll do; so, mount up with wings like eagles above the boisterous clouds."
—from a song by Alma Welch

Chapter Five

Invisible Pain

~∰⊙

When someone said that she was "thankful to have pain," it
made me do a double take. You say, "Unbelievable!" Not
according to a retired missionary nurse friend, Mrs. Neva J. Thompson, who stated: "The greatest problem with lepers is that they
do *not* feel pain. They know nothing is wrong, nor that they have a
disease until a foot, hand, or any part of the affected body does *not*
feel pain if burned or injured."

My friend, Mrs. Thompson, worked with some leprosy (Hansen's
disease) patients in India and also in Carville, Louisiana. She ex-
plains why lepers do not feel pain: "Leprosy destroys the sensory
nerve so they are without feeling while fingers and toes are destroyed.
It made me *thankful for pain*, because it is a protection to us." The
damage caused by Hansen's disease does eventually become apparent. However, this disease has almost disappeared in the United States
because of modern treatment and control.

Leprosy, diabetes, cancer, arthritis, or a severe headache are
just some of the painful problems that can easily be invisible. One
may be suffering from deep emotional pain, concealing all symptoms of an aching heart. Fighting back tears, running away to a
quiet place, or masking the agony of that stabbing inner pain may

itself be unbearable. When this masked pain continues, it may create a physical problem of dire consequence. Enduring pain in silence over a prolonged period may manifest itself in an unforeseen physical dilemma.

Diabetes: Another Insidious Disease

Diabetes has been called an insidious disease. It may be invisible at first, because it does not always become evident until damage has been done in some part of the body. Symptoms may be hidden, both from the individual and from others. Even after diagnosis, it may continue to be invisible. Diabetes is a metabolic disorder that prevents the body from keeping a healthful level of sugar in the blood. Therefore, the body can not properly use energy from food, which is as essential as the air we breathe. Diabetes can be detected by blood or urine tests. Once the disease is diagnosed, treatment is begun to control the blood sugar level. Since there is no cure for diabetes, and the body can no longer work automatically to regulate its own glucose, serious, long-term health problems may develop if the blood glucose level is not controlled by other means.

Because diabetes is an invisible disease, some people are neglectful of medical advice and may not feel pain or show any visible sign of this disease; thus, they may not follow the proper diet or their prescribed program. They may want to deny any health problem and act like any healthy person. Neglecting to control diabetes may lead to such serious complications as retinopathy (eye problems, which can lead to blindness), nephropathy (kidney disease, which can lead to kidney failure), or neuropathy (a serious nerve disorder affecting the entire body). Many of the other complications associated with diabetes may be heart attack, stroke, liver disorders, coma, and frequent infections. Sometimes foot or leg amputations are necessary. Some adolescents with diabetes avoid letting their friends know they are on a restricted diet or on insulin therapy. They don't want to be different. But, wanting to do as everybody else does—eating fast foods and simple sugar foods, for example—may lead to behavior devastating to a person with diabetes.

When I worked for a physician in Los Angeles, we received some shocking news one morning. Early that day before school, one of our teenage diabetics had jumped off a bridge, thus abruptly ending what could have been a happy, wholesome life.

Why?

What could have been done to help this young man? How could we have convinced him and his family of the value of working closely with his doctor, dietitian, nurse, and the diabetes class educator?

Actually, everything in our office had been done that could have been. Acceptance of his disease was difficult for him and for his parents. He looked healthy and had been an athletic boy, but he and his family never kept their appointments with the health-care team. The few times he saw the doctor, his blood sugar level was high. His doctor pleaded with the boy's parents to learn about this disease and the program that should be followed, but to no avail. They endured greater pain as a consequence of a failure to understand or see the traumatic and invisible pain of their son. In this case, and there are many more, an invisible and insidious disease led to a tragic ending.

Well-meaning family, friends, church members, neighbors, and acquaintances can create more pain by inattention than the actual disease of an individual can. In some cases, they may not know the invisible, insidious aspects of a person's health problems. Pain is hurting, and the inner pain is severe. Pain can be a challenge. But, we who live in chronic pain can live above it as countless others do every day. That is the purpose of this book.

Arthritis: Another Insidious Disease

My experience with arthritis is one example of an invisible, insidious disease. I have osteoarthritis, which is a chronic disease requiring daily treatment. The Arthritis Foundation has reported in a booklet, *Taking Charge—Learning to Live with Arthritis*, that over 36 million Americans suffer one of the more than one hundred types of arthritis and other rheumatic diseases. This Arthritis Foundation booklet further states:

The physical effects of arthritis can change from day to day, and even from hour to hour. Living with an uncertain future is very difficult. . . .

No one can predict when flare-ups of arthritis will happen or how long they will last. . . .

Everyone feels pain differently. Because no one can actually see pain, others may not understand how it affects you. Just as people feel pain differently, they also respond to it differently. . . .

Negative attitudes in others create a difficult problem that we people with arthritis face constantly. We have to deal with these negative attitudes or ignore them, and this in itself presents a danger. The Arthritis Foundation booklet gives valuable information on this subject. The following excerpts from this booklet have been of great help to many victims with arthritis to accept these negative situations that create such inner pain:

- People with arthritis often tire easily and may not be able to participate in all the activities they once enjoyed. . .
- You can reduce fatigue by learning to pace yourself throughout the day. . .
- Develop priorities for yourself as you go through the day. . .
- Don't try to hide the fact that you are tired or can't do certain tasks. If you do try to cover up, not only might you damage your joints, but your family and friends might develop unrealistic expectations of you.

The Arthritis Foundation books and other publications have helped me in learning to cope with this disease, which is many times invisible to others. The Arthritis Foundation's address is included in the listing of various organizations in this book's appendix.

A Traumatic Experience with Cancer
Each Sunday our nation is privileged to have a TV speaker who eloquently upholds the moral values and faith of our forefathers. As we watch this renowned gentleman, Dr. D. James Kennedy, proclaim his message, we do not know the distressing pain he may

be enduring or the traumatic pain he has experienced. Dr. Kennedy has written the following especially for this book:

> While throughout most of my ministry, I have had to deal with excruciating physical pain in the form of asthma and severe headaches (for which I must have medication available on my person at all times), I have also suffered constantly from a back injury early in life and from the surgical fusion of the cervical vertebrae, which failed to correct a neck problem. When these decide to act up in unison, the pain can be disabling.
>
> But I must confess that the most intense pain I have experienced was the emotional trauma I had to undergo while a young married student working on an advanced degree at the Chicago Graduate School of Theology. I was sitting in the lobby of a hospital where my wife, Anne, had been taken for what we presumed was a routine biopsy. After the report came back from the laboratory, the doctor came out to see me. I will never forget the staggering impact that his words had on me. He had told us previously that in 99 percent of cases like hers, the tumor proved to be benign. But he walked right up to me and said, "Your wife has cancer." If this doctor, who was a huge man, weighing about 250 pounds, had walked up and hit me in the stomach with his fist, the impact would have been no different.
>
> As I stood there, the room seemed to spin around and around. He must have talked for about two minutes as he asked for my permission to proceed immediately with the surgery. My head was swimming all that time, and I was losing touch with my environment. As soon as the doctor left, I literally dove for a nearby couch and passed out like a light. I never realized before that mere words could carry such a physical impact. And later, I think that perhaps the most difficult task that has ever fallen to me was that of breaking the unexpected news to my wife. I looked at her on that bed, realizing that she was unaware of her condition and expected to rise up and go home at any minute. She looked at me and said, "It is benign, isn't it?"
>
> And I said, "No, dear, I'm afraid it's cancer." Never have I felt words shaped so sharply into a knife; I felt like Abraham—as if I had driven that blade into her heart. But I want you to know that knife was driven deep into my heart as well. It plunged down into

my very soul. Like Lincoln, upon hearing of the death of his son, I felt like saying: "I think that I shall never be glad again."

But Anne and I learned through that awful experience that God in His infinite wisdom sometimes uses pain to give us His most enduring blessings like songs of praise in the night.

—D. James Kennedy, Ph.D., *Coral Ridge Ministries,*
Fort Lauderdale, Florida

Back Pain—Another Invisible Pain

Back pain is an anguish most everyone has experienced. It may occur with fatigue, fever, pregnancy, and other ailments. It sometimes is a symptom of some disorder in the body, such as a spinal tumor, or maybe kidney disease. An injury to the back is one of the most common causes for backache. I have lived with terrible back pain for over twenty years and have had two back surgeries. But at times I wish I had never had the surgeries, for the pain is so severe. There is for me, the added pain of countless arthritic spurs and sciatica.

A dear friend has described her suffering and trauma from a back problem as follows:

My worst experience with physical pain came at a terrible time in my life. It's not that there are ever good times in one's life for suffering or debilitation; however, as a wife and a mother to two young children of seven and eight, my services were more in demand. Beyond what would be considered the norm for most mothers at that stage, the Lord had led our family in the direction of homeschooling. The demands on my personal involvement were even greater.

My pain came in the form of a bulging disc problem in the lower lumbar area of my back. I'd had short bouts with the spasm that accompanies this type of problem, and they had always been overcome with medicine, rest, and caution. In the winter of 1992, it developed into a prolonged situation when the temporary therapies were not successful. Ultimately, the disc scarred onto the sciatic nerve, and surgery was required.

By August of '92, surgery was scheduled, baby sitters were arranged, registration was completed, and I was prepped and awaiting an available operating room. Suddenly it was halted when a blood test showed that I was pregnant! We were shocked, excited, and concerned! I was thirty-seven years old! I had been through a battery of tests and X-rays. The unborn baby was about four weeks old during these tests.

One of our greatest blessings was that our neurosurgeon was a man who valued life as God-given at any stage of existence, and the word "abortion" was never mentioned. Our surgeon alleviated our concerns about harm done to the baby, and our excitement was unmatched! The pregnancy was not an easy one. Our schooling at home consisted of the girls' climbing into our bed next to me while I read to them. I gave up teaching my class at church and attending church services because sitting was not to be endured. How could this be God's will for a homeschooling mom and pastor's wife, now pregnant! I knew the Lord could remove my physical problem, and I prayed that He would. Eventually, I had to accept my situation as God's will.

The pain went even deeper. She opened her heart about the accompanying suffering she endured because her health problem was invisible. There is a major emotional problem that often occurs because of the lack of understanding by our family and friends. Because some sufferers are able to *mask* their pain, the observers lose their empathy, giving the sufferer the feeling of being disbelieved. If only they could give an open expression of understanding by helping in some tangible activity! She continues:

There is a phenomenon that occurs in a situation with prolonged pain, which I believe is common. Over a period of some time, the onlookers generally lose sympathy for the one suffering. Very likely, it is due to the victim's success in dealing with the pain, and the observer's inability to perceive that great effort is constantly taking place. Most people dealing with prolonged pain, desperately long for a "normal" life again, and they don't want undue amounts of sympathy. If they feel they must constantly explain themselves, it serves as a damaging blow to their healthy reserve of self-respect. Often the sufferer will attempt to accomplish things they should not.

When you think about it, immense amounts of sympathy and understanding flow when we see someone suffering intense, short-term pain. Even when there is little pain occurring at the time, sympathy is evoked when there is something *visual* to relate to—such as a cast, a hospital room, etc. When the pain endures over a longer period of time and the sufferer learns to work at living a "normal" existence, the experience is moved *under* the surface.

I was encouraged by Paul's testimony that God's grace was sufficient for me. The Lord really spoke to me through Job's testimony. Job never knew the purpose of his suffering! He never knew that Satan had been allowed to approach God, nor that God had chosen to use him as an object lesson on faithfulness to the kingdom of Satan and to future believers. For all of Job's questions about why, the Lord never saw fit to reveal to him the vantage point He gave to us on Job's situation. Yet Job held strongly throughout the fog that his God was good and faithful and was a loving God, and He would never violate His own perfect character. He could be trusted!

—*Esther Pfrimmer, Hiram, Georgia*

Many Die Never Revealing Their Suffering

Day after day, relatives, friends, and acquaintances are diagnosed as suffering from an invisible disease. It is sad when the person is dying, or even dead, before we learn the anguish that had been hidden. It is then too late to be more considerate, caring, or loving.

When I was an outpatient at Mayo Clinic, Rochester, Minnesota, I met a lovely couple who lived in Rochester. They both looked the "picture of health" and were outgoing and interested in doing things for me. Their appearance did not reveal the underlying pain they carried, as told now by Fred's wife, Vivian:

What stands out in my memory as the beginning of my most painful experience is the day we decided to take my little dog, Zoobee, along for a ride with us. We needed to make a trip to a nearby town where my husband would have a routine chiropractic treatment. It was a warm, spring afternoon, so instead of just waiting for Fred to come out, I hooked the leash to Zoobee's harness, and we were off for our walk. I thought, *she sure looks like she feels a lot better than I do today.* Then I allowed myself to put into concrete thought something that had been in the back of my mind for weeks, maybe months.

I wonder if I might have cancer somewhere in my body, and I'm slowly dying? I was forty-two at the time and felt generally good except for some recently noticed digestive problems, such as multiple trips to the bathroom in the mornings before leading normal, healthy, active afternoons. To be on the safe side, I made an appointment to see my doctor at the clinic in our small Wisconsin town, just to be sure it wasn't gallstones. We had planned to make a trip to Wyoming for a deer hunting trip with our son, who was a senior in high school. I didn't want to get far from home and be rushed off for surgery in a strange place.

At the clinic, the ultrasound test was performed, with searching, studying, stopping, and looking more deeply. Then a more experienced adviser was called. Lots of silence. The next morning, my doctor called and said I needed a CAT scan. Donna, my best friend at the time, couldn't see the sense of making the trip to Rice Lake, because I *looked* the picture of health. And she just knew it was another needless test, costing time and money—but she agreed to go with me. In the late afternoon the next day, my doctor called just as my truck-driver husband walked in from his week on the road. My doctor asked if I could come to his office right away. He greeted us in his office with these piercing words: "We have found tumors in your pancreas. A large one in front, another at the end, and others in between. We suspect pancreatic cancer. We can do a bypass to make your last days easier."

His words, "make your last days easier" rang through my mind. Did Fred hear that? Maybe I should just keep quiet and not imagine he said those words. Praise God! Those words were spoken *thirteen years ago!* Fred is of German descent, so his emotions are very controlled. He seldom acts with feeling about anything unless it is carefully thought through first. I've learned this behavior from him, although I'm of French heritage, and we are emotional about everything!

Mostly I felt abandoned, but I did not feel forsaken, because of Christ as my personal Savior. There was a feeling of total peace, of course, mingled with frightful emotional anguish. When I returned home, people started praying. I called two friends who were registered nurses. Both of them said the same thing, "Go big, and go now. Don't wait another day!"

The instinct of self-preservation prevailed, however, and I called my doctor. My doctor said, "I have a brother who works in pathology at the Mayo Clinic in Rochester. I'll call him." He did, and the next day I received a call from one of the doctors at Mayo Clinic asking that I be there the next day. It usually takes out-of-state people a month to get an appointment at Rochester. My doctor has saved my life four times now. He is world-renowned, yet when he talks to you, because he cares, you feel as if you are the only other person in the world.

He came into my room with a number of students, who he had with him most of the time. Before I left home, one of my nurse-friends had said, "Now, when you get to the Mayo Clinic, make those doctors talk to you. Be sure you ask them, 'What would you do if I were your wife or daughter?'" When my doctor said, "Well, Dear Lady, what are we going to do about that pancreas?" I knew what to say, so I asked, "What would you do if I were your wife or daughter?" His split-second hesitation assured me he would be honest with me. He replied, "I'd take it out." With no hesitation, I answered, "Let's do it!"

He proceeded to make the arrangements for the earliest date possible. I rested in perfect peace that night for the first time since I had received the bad news, because I knew that all that could be done, would be done for me. I had confidence in my doctor.

My husband wrote something on a piece of paper and stuck it on my hospital room wall. What comfort when I read what he had written: "Fear not, for I am with you. Do not be dismayed; I am your God. I will strengthen you; I will help you; I will uphold you with my victorious right hand" (Isa. 41:10 TLB).

What comfort to read those words! I had His perfect peace. I had no other choice, and I knew I was in the hands of the Lord. Another reason I rested so peacefully that night was because of the prayers of the people, which had begun with the onset of my terrible shock. Those prayers helped me to trust the doctors and to know that God calls doctors just like He calls preachers, missionaries, or anyone into His ministries.

Well, my surgery took about seven hours. About 5 P.M., the surgeon called my husband from the operating room. The message was, "We've found cancer, and now we're deciding what to do." Two hours later, I was wheeled out. My husband thought I might really die. He said it was the first time he would have said I looked bad in the twenty-two years of our marriage, and I'm not a gorgeous person as is. The surgeon spoke to my husband, saying, "She came through OK, but now there are only about a million things that could go wrong." *Nothing did!* Praise the Lord!

I opened my eyes in intensive care. A huge wall clock pointing to 10:00 was the first thing I saw; I didn't know whether it was A.M. or P.M. And, listen to this—next to the clock was a sign that read "Today is the first day of the rest of your life."

Next, I experienced something my doctor has since told me was "ghost pain." The "ghost" was my doctor's scalpel moving carefully across my abdomen. I actually thought I was experiencing the surgery and felt pain as if it were reality. I raised my arms as high as I could and gained the attention of my nurse. He brought me a pad and pencil. I wrote: *pain.*

"Well, I'll give you something for that, and you won't feel a thing."

I never felt the "ghost pain" again. However, I had become more aware of the fact that I could not breathe. I raised my arms again; the nurse brought me the pad and pencil. In terrible script I wrote: *I can't breathe.* The nurse said, "Mrs. Rye, that's because the machine is breathing for you. If you be quiet and lie still, we'll take that tube out very soon."

I learned that when one is on a respirator, and one begins to breathe on one's own, the lungs fight the machine, and they cancel each other out, causing a feeling of being smothered. If one lies still and quiet, the machine will breathe for you. Still, this it is not easy to do. That was my first surgery in 1984. My husband and I moved to Rochester to be near the doctors at the Mayo Clinic, as it was important for me to have routine checkups.

Now thirteen years later, I am still alive. I am in wonderful pain-free health, until the cancer comes back, which has happened almost like clockwork every three years since 1984. I have had two liver tumors that occurred at separate times following the pancreatic cancer in 1984. Thank God, they always get all of it. My doctors say it's that type. Surgery always gets it, and I never have had chemotherapy.

Now I know that "nothing is impossible with God" (Luke 1:37 NIV). This is a real blessing. Always after each surgery recovery, I am in pain-free health. What a marvelous God to be so good to me! I give Him the praise and the thanks. "What time I am afraid, I will trust in thee" (Ps. 56:3 KJV).

My doctors tell me there is really nothing I can do as far as prevention, since the type cancer I have is not affected by diet or drastic treatments. Empathically, I thank God for giving me thirteen-plus years of life. Most pancreatic cancer patients die within two years of diagnosis. Most do not even make it back for their first checkup. "Oh, that men would praise the Lord for his goodness, and for his wonderful works to the children of men" (Ps. 107:8,15,21,23 KJV).

These days I spend much time reading God's holy Word. First and Second Peter and First, Second, and Third John encourage me by letting the Holy Spirit speak to me. Luke 23 tells of the resurrection and ascension of Christ, and I claim His promises of someday being with Him.

"In My Father's house are many mansions; if it were not so, I would have told you. I go to prepare a place for you. And if I go and prepare a place for you, I will come again and receive you unto Myself, that where I am, there you may be also" (John 14:2–3 NKJV).

—*Vivian A. Rye, Rochester, Minnesota*

Step by step, Vivian has taken us through the invisible and insidious pain she has suffered. In January 1997, Vivian was diagnosed with cancer of the right lung and liver. This time, nothing can be done for her but to wait on the Lord to do His will in her life. She is having pain as of this writing. "At times," she says, "the pain becomes quite a burden."

Vivian has written a letter to her physician, dated January 16, 1997, and has given permission to print it without using his name:

Dear Dr.————:

This is to thank you for the thirteen years of pain-free, joyous life you have given me and for all you did during those years that was above and beyond the call of duty, which gave me the courage to keep up the battle against the problem that was trying to kill me. This is also about something I have wanted to tell you, but not on our professional office time. It has to do with eternity. I have never asked you what religious background you have, but I know from things you've said that you believe in God. Actually, this is not about religion. It's about a person. It is about someone we can know personally and talk with as we would with a good friend who cares profoundly about our well-being. I thought growing up that I would go to heaven or, at least, I hoped I would. Then someone told me there is a way we can know for sure before we come to the end of our life . . .

Now that I know, I want to share this with as many people as possible. The way is simply to believe what the Bible says about Jesus being the Son of God—actually God incarnate—and that He died on the cross as the atonement for our sins past, present, and future. It seems just too easy to believe, but that is what the Bible—God's Word—says to us in John 3:16. So now, Dear Doctor, when I look at death, it is not with dread. Now it is like looking at a glorious sunrise with unfathomable promise. There is no way I can thank you for what you have given me.

Yours very truly,
Vivian A. Rye

Her letter made a profound impact upon me as these words poured out from the depth of her heart and inner soul. Realistically, she knows only what the doctors tell her—and that is very bleak. But she knows that God is in control. Vivian is only one of thousands of people walking the streets today who carry inside their feelings of wondering what the future holds in their life on this earth.

May these three people who have shared their painful experiences help us, not knowing what may be hidden, to be more aware and sympathetic towards others. These individuals exemplify persons of strong, intense faith, knowing that God is sovereign.

To people, their pain was invisible, but to God their suffering was under His loving scrutiny. They learned that trusting God during such difficult times was their only comfort, peace, strength, and confidence. Their complete reliance on the Almighty God was attested to by their written declaration of faith that their pain was *not* invisible to Him. Their hope was demonstrated by their great expectation in the spiritually beneficial outcome of each painful experience.

"Now faith is the substance of things hoped for, the evidence of things not seen . . . he is a rewarder of them that diligently seek him" (Heb. 11:1,6*b* KJV).

Nothing is invisible to God and nothing is impossible with God. But none of us can know the pain that is behind each face. That outward appearance may conceal some deep hidden suffering. Just remember: Until you have walked in my shoes and I have walked in yours, neither of us can know the other's pain.

Invisible pain? Yes, to us human beings on this earth, but not invisible to the omnipotent One!

Chapter Six

Refusing to Give Up

~∰◞

Do you or a loved one have diabetes? Then this may be of help to you and may turn an unpleasant way of life into a rewarding and joyful one. Norman Beard has proved in his struggles with diabetes that nothing can keep him down. As you approach his home, his joyful singing will likely reach your ears before you see him.

Before his blindness, Norman played his own guitar. But now he only uses backup music, or a friend plays for him. One of his favorite songs is "Don't Give Up," and he has written it from his heart and experience: "Sometimes your life is troubled, sometimes your life is pain; sometimes all you see is rain; sometimes your life's a winter; sometimes your life's a fall; sometimes you wonder if it's anything at all. Don't give up—there is still hope for you! Don't give up—God's still there for you!"

Diagnosis Diabetes

Norman has granted permission for the above, from one of his album songs, to be reprinted here. He has shared also his life story for this publication. I consider his contribution a highlight in helping achieve the intention of this book—to help others cope with pain.

Norman was a rebellious teenager. At age fourteen, he began having blurry vision and was prescribed glasses. Only a week later, his mother noticed he was losing weight and drinking water excessively. Every night he took a pitcher of water to his room to help quench his thirst. His mother became aware of his unusual symptoms and took him to a doctor.

The doctor recognized the symptoms and hospitalized him with the diagnosis of diabetes. Insulin injections began, and, using an orange as a simulator, he was taught how to give his own injections. I am told patients now inject themselves with normal saline as practice for insulin. As long as he took his insulin, his diabetes didn't show any problems, so he never went to a doctor, nor had any blood sugar tests. Neither he nor his family received any diabetes education. He coasted along in life as a teenager, trying to keep up with his friends.

He said he went into a life of drunkenness, drug abuse, thievery, and immorality. He never went to church and said he didn't know the name "Jesus" until he went to a church service in Meridian, Mississippi, when he was twenty-two years old. He excitedly told this story:

> In an instance, Jesus changed me completely. I remember the next blessing from the Lord was a beautiful, loving wife, Sandy. He blessed me again with a beautiful daughter, Reba. Then the Lord called me to preach. Man, I was excited to preach the Good News of Jesus. But I made a terrible mistake. I thought that my relationship to God was based totally on what I did. I thought that if I did a lot of good things today, and not so many bad things the next day, I was OK. When I started preaching, all I could preach were the rules. By the time I got through preaching, no one in the church was going to make it to heaven. I wasn't going there, either, and I was the pastor!

His voice revealed the depth of his anguish as he spoke of those pastoral days. He recalled his struggles and self-righteous feelings:

> You can imagine what it was like sitting under my teaching and preaching week after week after week. I thought I was

successful and that I was preaching the Word. I'd leave the church satisfied by my living up to the rules that I told my congregation they had to live up to.

At twenty-eight years of age, he preached on Sunday and worked full time during the week as a diesel mechanic. While lying on a creeper under a truck one day, he passed out. When he was revived, he knew something was drastically wrong. He had been a diabetic for fourteen years, and he realized he had not "taken real good care of myself."

When he arrived at the doctor's office in critical condition, he says his blood pressure was about 280/160, and the doctor wondered how he made it without being brought in on a stretcher. The news was devastating: his kidneys were failing; his blood pressure and blood sugar were out of control; his eyes were blurry.

He remembers lying in the hospital one day and reaching to turn on the TV. The picture was blurry, but he and the doctor had both thought that the blurry vision was a side effect of medication. The condition persisted when he left the hospital, so he went to an eye doctor. After the eye examination, the doctor only said, "Boy, your eyes are a mess. You need to see a specialist!"

It was during this painful time with his eyes that he had another blessing in his life—a little baby, Nathaniel, called Nathan. Norman was thrilled with his baby son, but he was bitter about his horrible suffering. He had strong reason to be nervous, irritable, and upset. When one is in constant agony with a screaming body, the nerves become sensitive and frayed. He did not realize that his body was filling with poison from his failing kidneys.

When he saw the specialist, the specialist said, "Your eyes are a mess, but I think we can save them." Yet, after twenty-three laser surgeries, his eyes continued getting worse. By this time, anger, all against God, was building up inside Norman. He blamed God and he had no regret for his neglect in caring for his diabetes, which helped bring on the consequences of a damaged, out-of-control diabetic body. He felt God was unfair. Norman said he had kept all the rules that he had preached, so his thoughts were that God was punishing him with blindness, kidney failure, and suffering. He had a wife, a little girl, and a baby son. He says:

> I was just starting the American dream of getting my own home and falling in to the footsteps of my own dad. Everything was going well, and suddenly, I was flat on my back and losing my eyesight. You know, when you feel like God doesn't love you, you don't really care if anybody else does. When you think God is mad at you, you don't care if you are mad at anybody else. I fell into a deep depression and locked myself in my bedroom.
>
> I had a lot of friends come by to see me to try to cheer me up. I even had some of Job's friends come by. You probably think they are gone, but they are not; they are still around. I had a lot of people say, "I think you have sinned the sin unto death. Norman, you just need to repent and you'll get better." So I would repent, repent, and repent until my repenting was just worn out. I had another friend come by. He said, "Well, I think you are just full of demons, and we just need to cast them out."
>
> I told him to get them out, that I was ready. He looked into my eyes and said, "Yep, I see them in there!" I was ready for anything, so I told him to get rid of them. He prayed for me, or prayed on me, or did something like that. But I didn't get any better; in fact, I think I got a little worse. So I went into my bedroom and lay back down. I decided I would just make them so mad at me that they wouldn't come back. I began treating everybody badly and told them I didn't need them around me and that I didn't need God anymore. I resigned as pastor of my church; I took "Reverend" off my name at the mailbox, and the minister sticker off my car. I turned my Christian radio station off, and I put my Bible away. I said that if this is the way God is, and if this is love, I don't want anything to do with it. I just lay in my bed because I was so angry and bitter.
>
> My wife thought it would be best to send my kids off to some relatives. I just screamed at them all the time. So my kids were taken away and it was just my wife and me. She watched me deteriorate. My kidneys finally shut down completely and they started me on dialysis. I was able to do it at home. I wasn't on a machine; I was on CAPD (continuous ambulatory peritoneal dialysis), and my wife was doing it for me. I was too sick

and too blind to do it for myself. They were continuing to work on my eyes, but I was terribly depressed. I remember my wife came to me one day and said, "Norman, if you don't go to the hospital now, I think you are going to die right here in bed."

I just told her, "Whatever . . ." I had really given up, and I didn't really care. I was lying in bed in a fetal position. They took me to the hospital and I was in there twenty-one days. I had tubes hanging out of me. I was so weak from the dialysis and all the pain in my eye. I had glaucoma; my eyeball pressure was supposed to be seven to fourteen, but my eyeball pressure was in the eighties and nineties. That is how hard the eyeball was; the pain was killing me.

While I was in the hospital, I also got peritonitis, an infection in the abdominal cavity from which you usually die, and it almost killed me. I got it from a tubing that the nurse dropped on the floor. Then she put the "sterile" port in backwards, which was left exposed. My wife noticed that it was not hooked up right when she came into my room shortly afterwards, but within two hours I was deathly ill! Because of the peritonitis, I got esophagitis, and I just kept getting worse. The doctor told my wife she should call the family in because "Norman has about twenty-four hours left; he has given up. I can't do a thing for him."

My wife came into my room, and I remember like it was yesterday. She grabbed my hand and said, "Norman, it is up to you now, if you want to live or die. The doctors have done all they can do." And, to this day, I don't really understand what it was, or how it was that I made the decision that I made. But I told my wife, "I want to live, Honey." The next day they scheduled my surgery; they removed my right eye. I knew when they took that eye out that I was going to be totally blind, but I wanted to live. I remember waking up after surgery, and I was pain free for the first time in probably a year.

I remember three days after leaving the hospital, I washed my car, and a week later, I went to the grocery store with my wife. She dragged me around, hanging onto the buggy, but I was up and moving around. However, I was still depressed. You see, I did not have any joy in my life. I think now about how many people that I meet that are in the church, and they are there because it is the thing to do. They have no joy or excitement. I didn't have any either.

About two months after my eye surgery, Christmas Eve 1989, I got a phone call from the Kidney Donor Center. The person said, "Mr. Beard, we have a kidney for you. It is a perfect match; it's one in a chance of 300,000 that you will ever get a perfect match. Do you want it?"

I said, "Yes!"

Man, we had a madhouse: Kids opened Christmas presents, family members came and got the kids, and then we left for Birmingham. At the hospital, they were preparing me for surgery. A nurse came into my room—now remember, I am totally blind—and said, "Mr. Beard, I've got to shave you from your nipples to your knees." I said, "*Everything*?" She said, "Yes." What could I say but, "OK". I also experienced enemas for the first time!

They got me all ready for surgery and then called it off. I said, "Way to go, God!" You know, that was the way it had been going for the last two years of my life. They had received a liver transplant for someone else and that took priority, so they put me off a day. The next day was a repeat preparation for surgery, which meant more enemas. But my blood sugar shot up to 1,300, so they said they could not do my surgery. Normal blood sugar is between 80 to 120, so they put me on a drip to get my sugar down.

When my blood sugar dropped, they wheeled me into a room for surgery and taped my head to the table. The kidney started working the instant they hooked it up. They wheeled me to intensive care, and in about three days, it stopped working! They didn't take the old one out; they just put the new one in front. Seven days it stayed there! The doctor said, "In seven days we are going to biopsy the kidney to see if it is dead."

Discouraged, I said, "It is probably dead." A couple of sisters in town had been praying; they prayed over a cloth and brought it to me. They said, "Here put this under your pillow." I said, "OK. Nothing else works."

On the morning of the seventh day, the kidney started working. Thank God, eight years later it has not stopped, slowed down, or missed a beat since that time! And I am on less anti-rejection medication than most kidney transplant patients because it was a perfect match. But I was still depressed; I had no joy. Sometimes, circumstances in one's life can get better, but if the joy is gone, honey, it is gone. New cars, new houses, new husbands, won't give you joy. The Bible says in the Psalms that joy comes from one place—from the presence of the Lord. ". . . in thy presence is fulness of joy; at thy right hand there are pleasures for evermore" (Ps. 16:11*b* KJV).

But I had no joy during all that suffering. My favorite subject to talk about was death; I figured I would be checking out pretty soon. I was talking about it one of those bad days, you know. I told my aunt how it was going to happen to me and why it was going to happen, and Sandy, my wife, got fed up with it. She finally had about all she could take. So she said, "Let's go!" Now remember, I am totally blind; my wife does all the driving. I thought we were going home. The next thing I knew we were pulling up in a parking lot. Sandy said, "Get out. We are going to church."

"No, I don't think so, I said. "*Church* is the reason I am the way I am; *God* is the reason I am the way I am. I don't want to have anything to do with God." She dragged me into the church that I had pastored, and we sat in the back row. There was a young man, Ben, up there playing his guitar and singing. I love the guitar, but I was just sitting there and fuming! I was mad at Ben; I was mad at my wife; I was mad at God; and I was mad at the church.

When it came time for the invitation, my wife said, "Get up!"

"I am not going down there!"

My wife grabbed me, pulled me up off the pew and said, "We are going down front."

"I don't think so!"

But she said, "Yes, we are going down front!" And she told the young man that night that I needed joy and needed it right then.

I had never seen that guy before that night, and I didn't know what was going to happen. I wish I could have seen his face. Now please understand that I came from a charismatic background. Some may not know what that is. I had been prayed for every way imaginable. I had people trying to push me over, pick me up, cast things in, and cast things out, pray for every part of my body. People anointed with oil every part of my body that was permissible. I didn't have any idea what this guy was getting ready to do. I was standing there fuming and not happy about it. Oh, of all the things that Ben could have done! He reached out and hugged me. God hugged me through Ben! To this day it was like God was reaching out and hugging me through Ben and was saying to me, "I do love you; I still love you; I am not the one to blame for all these things that are happening to you."

I said, "God, if you love me, why doesn't everything go the way I want it to?" And then, *yes*, God hugged me through a man.

Oh, for the grace and mercy of God! Of anything this man could have done, he reached out and hugged me. God started a process in my life that night through a man, one that I didn't know. It was like a movie that I sometimes see when the little boy, trying to run away from his dad, maybe runs out into the traffic, or runs off the edge of the cliff, and his dad grabs him and holds him and won't let him go. The boy fights, kicks, screams, and bites, but the dad just holds on and won't let him go. That is kind of the way it was for me, as if God was holding me.

Finally, I just went limp and said, "God, I know you still love me." He loved me through a man; there were no lightning bolts or thunder that night, but I knew God still loved me. But how can God still love me? It was as if I were getting ready to go through one of the greatest tests in my life, probably even more so than losing all of my eyesight. As a diabetic, it is always dangerous if you get a sore, and I got a sore on my left big toe. When I went to the doctor, he cut a little off the toe. He thought it would get well, but it got worse. We kept working on it for months. Finally, I had some aggressive treatment in the hospital; they tried some skin graft on it, but that didn't work. I had blood poisoning! I knew the news was bad when they told me.

I asked my surgeon, Dr. Stephen Tart, a man that I love very much, "How much are you going to take off, Doc?" I was expecting him maybe to grab me on the ankle, and I knew I could live with that. But, I remember vividly, he grabbed me about three inches below the knee and said he would have to take it off up to that area. I will be honest with you, his words freaked me out and my wife also. But I told him, "OK, Doc, if that is what we have to do, then let's do it."

When he left, I told Sandy, "Honey, I need to be alone for awhile and you need to be alone too, so why don't you go home and spend the night there. I know you will be here with me for the next few nights, and you need all the rest you can get." She went home. I found out later that she spent about three hours screaming and crying.

I was lying in my hospital bed and thinking about the Lord and all He had done to restore my joy. Suddenly, I picked up the phone and called Sandy. "Honey, I want you to get my little tape deck and get our favorite tape. It's got some oldies on it, and I want you to bring it up to the hospital room." She came and I said, "Just push the play button and come here. I want to dance. This will be the last chance that I will ever have to dance with you . . ."

I am sure I looked a sight, standing in the hospital room with IVs hanging out of my arms, looking kind of ratty after being in there for three weeks, hanging onto my wife. We just held onto each other, slow dancing there in the middle of the hospital room, loving each other. I remember my wife whispered in my ear, "We'll do it again; we'll do it again." Then a nurse came into my room; she "lost it" and ran out.

I sat back down on my bed and told Sandy she needed to go, that I needed to spend some time with God. She left, and I grabbed my ankle. It sounds sort of funny, but I thanked my left leg for being what it had been to me. I had had this thing since I had been born, and I was sort of apologizing for the way things had turned out. Maybe it is hard to understand if you have never had anything amputated; your body parts are precious—take care of them.

Finally, I thanked God for loving me, and I went to sleep. The next day they did the surgery. It went well and I went home in a week. It took about one week for it to settle in what had really happened to me; my leg was gone, and it wasn't going to grow back. I remember getting in the shower and turning on the water fast and hard so my children wouldn't hear me cry. During one episode in the shower, I remember the Lord came to me, comforted me, and said, "I haven't changed! I am the same God I was before and I love you—and My grace is sufficient." I said, "I know, Lord, I know that You still love me." The Lord healed my heart; and it wasn't too long before I got fitted with my prosthesis. Shortly after, I was up walking around and doing everything that I was doing before I lost my left leg. I was healthy again and sharing the word of the Lord and getting opportunities to sing.

Then lo and behold, I found a sore on my right foot. I said, "*Oh, no!* Not again!" We treated this one a little bit differently.

For nine weeks, we drove to Jackson in the hot summer for hyperbaric oxygen therapy, which forced oxygen into my blood vessels to keep me from losing my right leg. I didn't lose this leg; all I lost was my big toe and a little part of my foot.

About fifteen months later, in November 1994, I started having some difficulty with my fingers. One of the worst things that can happen to a guitar player is that your fingers start going bad. I had used the guitar as an instrument of worship and praise, and I would use it sometimes just to vent my frustrations and confusion. I was not going to be able to do that any more. In the course of a few months, I had two fingers removed off my right hand. Then a few months later, I lost the ring finger on my left hand.

Norman always holds the attention of his audience, both young and old. He gives what he calls an "inventory" of himself. He starts at the top of his head and tells about his amputations.

- He has one eye but is totally blind
- Four fingers
- A kidney transplant
- No toes
- One leg

Then he praises God for *never* leaving him, His faithfulness, and for fulfilling all his dreams that he thought would never happen because of his illness. Norman knows the sufficiency and love of God, and he continues to give Him thanks for everything good. Norman continues his closeness to God with these sincere words:

> My wife and I are honest people with God, and we just let it out. If you would kinda trip out around our house sometimes, you would see how we are with God. He is there in the house with us, and we just tell Him out loud what is going on and how we feel. God knows us anyway. God has blessed me now and has given me an opportunity to record an album of songs that I have written over the last five years.

Norman has people laughing, and then crying, as he continues to tell of his many experiences, and he preaches at every opportunity. His song, "Don't Give Up," tells a lot about him, but there is another of his heartfelt songs that he has given permission to share. He does not give up in using every moment God has given him. He spends his time writing songs, singing praises, and proclaiming the word of God. Since I've met Norman and heard his life's story, the following song, "I'd Rather Be Blind," has become more meaningful to all who know him:

> You might think the only way to God is by your works; you might think the only way is from being good enough; you might think the only way is from doing what the preachers say; you might take a look at your life and say there ain't no way. But I'd rather be blind and know that I am loved; I'd rather be blind and know the Lord above; I'd rather be blind and not have my sight than to have two eyes and still not see the Light.

In a visit with Sandy, she said:

> The best thing I can say about all that has happened is that God has matured both of us in His love. We no longer cry and fume about our problems anymore, but we leave it in His hands. He gives us joy and peace in every circumstance we face. We find a lot of humor in whatever happens, and we can laugh about our problems now and know that God is still with us and loves us through it all. Ephesians 2:8–10 is the verse we lean on every day, because it is only by the grace of God that we have been able to get through all that has happened. Our walk with God is different every day; we just trust in Him.

Then Sandy opened the Bible and read: "For by grace are ye saved through faith; and that not of yourselves: it is the gift of God: Not of works, lest any man should boast. For we are his workmanship, created in Christ Jesus unto good works, which God hath before ordained that we should walk in them" (Eph. 2:8–10 KJV).

Norman related an incident about fulfilling his wish to dance again someday with his wife. About three months after his leg amputation, he had learned to walk on his prosthesis. They went to church and took his sound track. He told the congregation about the incident in his hospital room the night before his leg amputation and then asked his wife to come forward. He told the sound track man to start the selected tape. Norman's own words finish this story:

> My wife and I danced again in the church as best we could. I, with my fake leg, tried not to bruise her feet. We cried and cried, and the people cried. God was glorified. Why? Because the joy of the Lord is my strength!
>
> God is good, and I am a walking testimony of the grace of God. I haven't done anything to deserve it. I told God to leave me alone, to get out of my face. He said, "No, I adopted you! I love you! You are mine!" God says you are saved by grace and you are kept by grace, and His grace will take you to heaven. I don't know how much longer I have left, but I've told God that I am going to pour out my life for people as long as I have life in my body. People are going to hear of the grace and mercy of God. I don't know exactly what the future holds for me, but one thing I know, God has shown Himself faithful. And I'd rather be blind and know the Lord above!
>
> — *Norman Beard, Meridian, Mississippi*

Norman is active with the American Diabetes Association as the publicity and public relations coordinator in his area at the time of this writing. Norman spends a lot of time at his church counseling people over the telephone, or in whatever ministry he can perform. His positive attitude and endurance of suffering is a testimony to the strength and joy that only God can give. Every person with diabetes should learn from Norman's sufferings that his life could have been different *if* he had learned to do the things that all diabetics are taught by their doctor and in the available classes. As told in the chapter, "Invisible Pain," diabetes is an insidious disease, and most people with diabetes can control this disease as a way of life *if* the proper instructions are followed.

It is advisable for a person with diabetes to wear a medical identification bracelet or necklace at all times. Lives have been saved because of the vital information that can be immediately available for medical attendants. (See Medic Alert in the appendix.)

May the Lord give you wisdom and guidance to do what you should, so your life may glorify Him. Your life can be beautiful and a blessing if you wait on God to help you soar on eagles' wings.

Chapter Seven

A Mother's Love for a Special Child

M ost everyone had heard of a certain mother with a Down syndrome child in the community where I retired. Only this special person was not a child; she was in her twenties. She was not only a "special child," but she had lived beyond her anticipated life expectancy. Usually that was expected to be in the teens, but now with advances in medical and improved long-term care facilities, people with Down syndrome may survive beyond their early middle age.

It has been reported that about one in 800 babies born is affected by Down syndrome and is usually recognized soon after birth. About forty years ago, the cause was unknown, but now it is said to be caused by chromosomal abnormality. At birth, some of the characteristics may be a flat face, slanting eyes, short and broad hands, short and thick feet, the tongue large and thick, and some tongues may tend to protrude. Because of their physical features, most of them usually are recognizable, but each one has an individual personality. About 40–50 percent are born with a heart defect, and most are susceptible to any illness.

They are cheerful, affectionate, and have a lot of love to offer anyone who takes time to know them. Everyone needs to experience sharing love with such a friendly, caring child. This particular child that I met had an especially amazing mother whose gentle, caring ways were evident upon our first meeting. The only way I could meet Mrs. Wilma Meeker was to visit her home, as she never left her daughter. This mother's gentleness was evident, and her unwavering love to this special child lasted from her daughter's birth to her last breath, some thirty-five years later.

Parent's Devotion

At my request, Mrs. Wilma Meeker has written for this book the following life story of the pain, joy, and unusual moments she spent with her "angel":

My most painful experience is having a baby with Down syndrome. Kokette Ann was born November 23, 1959. The moment I saw her I knew something was wrong. She was blue and put in an oxygen tent. She didn't kick and move like other babies. She only moved in slow motion. Later the doctor came into my room and said my baby wasn't eating and that he had called in a specialist. The specialist came that day and explained to me about a disease called Down syndrome. I was in shock! He told me that my husband and I should think of an institution. Furthermore, he told me that my baby girl would probably never reach her teenage years. I felt I had had one blow after another. My head was whirling. My heart was broken. I felt my life was utterly shattered. How would I tell my husband?

Alvin, my husband, came into the hospital room happy and excited, his arms filled with gifts. I didn't want to tell him. But when he looked at me, he knew something wasn't right. I began sobbing as I told him the doctor's report. My husband looked at me and said, "Dear, let's turn everything over to the Lord. We will *not* put our baby girl into an institution. We will keep her, love her, and do everything we can. . . . We know the Lord gave her to us . . . He will give us wisdom to know what to do."

Within a few months after taking her home, we learned she had a hole in her aorta, the main artery that carries the blood from the heart. We gave her special attention at all times, and everyone in our hometown church in Canoga Park, California, loved her and joined us in a vigilant interest. I was with her night and day.

On three different mornings, I heard a man's voice calling, "Wilma, Wilma, Wilma!" But there was no one in the house with my baby and me. I continued taking care of the many duties with her, but I was in a panic state of mind. I felt the Lord was trying to get my attention for some reason. Then the thought hit me that I might be losing my mind.

One morning shortly thereafter, I awakened in deep depression and had a migraine. I felt utterly exhausted and could hardly lift my feet to do the necessary things for my baby. After she had fallen asleep, I pulled down the window shades, took the phone off the hook, fell on my knees, and cried out to the Lord to help me. I pleaded with the Lord to please let me know that everything would be all right with my baby. I cried and prayed until I was limp, silent, and lying on the floor on my face with my eyes closed. Then I had an awesome experience.

Large letters flashed vividly through my mind. I saw the words, "Be still and know that I am God." The words were huge. At that moment, perfect peace enveloped my entire mind and body! I jumped up, raised the window shades, put the telephone back on the hook, and felt like a new person. To this date, I have *never* had another migraine, nor depression! Then I realized that those words were the Lord's words: "Be still and know that I am God" (Ps. 46:10 KJV). He spoke to me from His Word. All I can say is hallelujah, what a Savior! I was not praying about my migraine or depression, but I had been praying and pleading for my Kokette Ann. But the Lord healed me and gave me new strength and a new outlook on the situation!

Later, the thought came to me, *What will happen to "Ko" if anything happens to Alvin or me? Who will care for my precious child?* I discussed this with my husband. He told me that he knew the Lord would leave one of us to care for her. A few days passed and my other daughter, Dee Ann, and her husband told me that they would take care of Ko if anything ever happened to us. Before Ko was two years of age, she was put on a tranquilizer. She was a very nervous child and was sickly all the time. She had all the childhood diseases and lived through them, but continued to have a nervous problem the rest of her life. We kept quiet around her and avoided any excitement. However, she amazed us when she stood up in her crib by herself by age two. She was walking by age two-and-a-half. That was a happy day for us!

At about age three, she was potty trained. One day I sat her on the stool and rested her little legs on a bench. I left her alone for just a few minutes. However, the next day her nose was red and swollen. We rushed her to the doctor, only to find that she had stuck toilet paper up both sides of her nose. What a relief and a lesson never to leave her alone again.

When she was about eleven years of age, she was running through the house one day and stumped her foot. She literally stopped walking. We took her to a specialist, and he found her instep was swollen. He put her foot in a cast for ten days. When he removed the cast, he convinced her that she could walk. She walked to the car, but she walked only on the ball of her foot. Nothing we did would get her to walk correctly. Finally, we had a therapist who came to our home with no success, and he said she had a "blocked mind" that she could not walk.

Furthermore, he said if she had any pain, then she would not cooperate. He felt the ligament would no longer work from lack of use and that if I could *ever* get her to walk forty-eight steps, I should be grateful. However, she would use a walker, and that was a blessing and a joy to all of us to see her up and moving.

Her daddy died in 1982 when Ko was twenty-three. What a painful day that was for me when I had to break the news to Ko on the way home from the funeral. I asked God to show me how to tell her. I remembered that she always loved *The Waltons* TV show, so I told her that her Daddy had gone to heaven to help Grandpa Walton build us a house. For years after Alvin died, she would watch when a car pulled into our yard and always say, "Oh, good, Daddy home now."

Years had passed when Ko demanded constant attention again. The doctor said she was living one minute at a time. When she was twenty-eight years old, she developed pneumonia, congestive heart failure, and an enlarged heart. She was extremely ill. While she was in the cardiac care unit and on a life-support system, a nurse told me one morning that Ko had already had an early visitor.

I was angry. I learned that the woman went past the nurse without speaking and walked to Ko's bed. She said a few words in a soft voice to Kokette and left. I asked the nurse to describe the woman to me. My family and I knew no one by that description. Why would a stranger do such an unusual thing, especially in the cardiac care unit? Later, with the description passing through my thoughts, a picture of my mother flashed through my mind. She had been dead for over forty years.

During this hospitalization of six weeks, it became necessary for Kokette to have a tracheotomy. The tube was left in her neck for weeks, even after she returned home. While she was in the hospital, she was placed on a rotating bed to help with her circulation and other needs. She had endured so much that she fought any one trying to help her, especially after coming home.

One night, I was utterly exhausted, mentally, physically, and emotionally. I felt as if I had weights on my feet. I was so very tired!

I was near her bed and grabbed hold of it to walk around the corner of it. But I felt as if I had bumped into someone. I looked in all directions but saw no one. There was no other person in the room; there was no object or wall near her bed. At that moment, a sudden surge of energy, strength, and peace flooded my body and soul! I knew the Lord was there. I felt His presence. I know He touched me and was making me aware of His presence. This was a confirmation to me that He was taking care of me in this extremely stressful situation.

My Ko's life was like a storybook. As her doctor said, her precious life was a "minute at a time." Nevertheless, I thank God for my Kokette.

I remember my husband always telling me before his death that Ko had brought our family closer together; we had adjusted our lives to hers. We have been blessed to have good doctors and wonderful friends and neighbors in both California and Mississippi.

Eight months before Kokette Ann was thirty-six years of age, she slipped out of her imprisoned body of suffering and severe limitations into a painless, joyful, everlasting life. I know that my little angel is now with our Lord, and I know that He will continue to help me endure the pain of a throbbing and empty void. My Ko is free of pain for the first time in her entire earthly life and now is whole and happy, running, and talking. And I know that we will all be together with Ko in heaven. I thank God for all the years He let our angel be with us.

Just a few days before she left us, the doctor met with me and the family. He told us that he had gone over all her records and that he was amazed that she had lived so many years, considering the many sicknesses she had had and that her heart was in a critical condition most of her life. But I think that God didn't want my Ko to suffer any longer, so He called her home.

At her funeral, The Reverend Dr. Reith Gewin's eulogy was comforting with the specially selected scripture he read. I would like to share some of these passages: "He that dwelleth in the secret place of the most High shall abide under the shadow of the Almighty. I will say of the Lord, He is my refuge and my fortress: my God; in him will I trust. . . . For he shall give his angels charge over thee, to keep thee in all thy ways" (Ps. 91:1–2,11 KJV).

And Psalm 46 has carried me through many dark and discouraging days, therefore, I requested this chapter be read at my precious angel's service: "God is our refuge and strength, a very present help in trouble. . . . Be still and know that I am God" (Ps. 46:1, 10a KJV).

KoAnn's sister, Dee Ann, wrote the following, which was read by the pastor: "To sum up in a few words, KoAnn touched everyone she met! You could not help but love her, protect her, and spoil her. She made my life full. If the Lord had not blessed me with her, I wouldn't be the person I am today.

She did the same with my children. They loved her as much as she loved them. They weren't afraid to show it, either. They brought their friends, boyfriends, and husbands to see her. She loved them all. She was stubborn, too. If she wanted things done her way, all she had to do was give you that look. It said, 'It's my way, or we'll negotiate.' I loved her more than life itself."

One of KoAnn's nieces, Lisa, wrote her thoughts, which he also read: "The memories are vast, but my main thought, or focus, right now is of KoAnn running hand in hand with Pa (KoAnn's daddy). She's laughing; she's running; she's peacefully happy."

Another one of KoAnn's nieces, Mandee, put her feelings into the following expressive words about her dear aunt: "KoAnn has always been such a special person to me, as well as to the people who made her a part of their lives. She was always making someone smile. We always had fun when we were together. There were people who felt uncomfortable around KoAnn. They would stare, laugh, or just look away. It never bothered KoAnn when people would glare at her. She would usually make a face at them, or just smile. I would get so tickled at these people's' faces. It was amazing how smart and perceptive she was. It was not her fault that she had Down syndrome, but God had a purpose for bringing her into this world.

KoAnn was such a child at heart. She was a thirty-five-year-old woman with a ten-year-old's heart. She loved watching cartoons and Disney movies. She had more Barbie dolls than she knew what to do with, and many crayons, notebooks, catalogs, and coloring books. She was real protective of her things. She was picky as to what we could play with and what we couldn't. She was the only thirty-five-year-old who still believed in Santa Claus. She loved getting up on Christmas morning and opening all her gifts.

Seeing her one last time was really difficult; she was finally at peace. Nothing will ever be the same again, but I know that I have had the best privilege of loving the most special child. Anyone that knew her will never be the same because they were touched by this incredible person."

I believe that others can better understand how to act, talk, and respond to people with Down syndrome or other afflictions by reading the way my family reacted to my special angel. If everyone would make an effort to associate with a disabled person, they would be blessed. They have the same feelings and emotions as others. They want to be treated like anyone else, and I pray that sharing my story will help make this possible. My granddaughter Lisa's poem speaks for all of us in the following tribute:

KoAnn

Known as KoAnn, she was the beauty throughout
our days,
Only kindness was within her, it showed in all
her ways,

Kid at heart, as were her thoughts, imagination
forever flows,
Eternally, her memory lives, as does our love
forever grow,
Endless are the days we'll mourn her absence in
our lives,
Always with us, God grant us the strength to
survive,
Memories to last a lifetime is the gift she left
behind,
Ever flowing in our thoughts, a kinder heart you
cannot find,
Endurance for sadness felt, wipe the tears, and
dry your eyes,
Knowing forever she's our angel flying high
above the skies,
Enable us to carry on, to live our lives complete,
Remember that our turn will come, again one day
we'll meet.

In loving memory of Kokette Ann Meeker, November 23, 1959–March
19, 1995.

—*Mrs. Wilma Meeker, Toomsuba, Mississippi*

Nothing more can be added to the loved ones' memories of
such a special child. I pray this touching story will cause others to
make a difference in the lives of the wanting-to-be-loved handicapped people. An affectionate smile, or even a small gift, can bring
happiness and help them forget someone else's stare or unthoughtful
action. It would help if parents would teach their children how to
react to anyone with an impediment. Life is short, and love makes
it happier, and maybe, seem longer while on this earth. God loves
them and wants to love them *through* us.

Chapter Eight

Sting of Death

To everything there is a season, a time for every purpose under heaven: a time to be born, and a time to die. . . . (Eccles. 3:1–2*a* NKJV)

King Solomon expressed some of his thoughts in the above writing. He was known as the "wisest man in the world," and also the richest king. He explored all the experiences of life and said there is "a time to die." Death is inevitable, but some people close their minds to the reality of death, saying it is too morbid to think about, too horrible to talk about, and they are just too busy to prepare for it. One never knows when death will strike, and some do not give it any thought.

Others look upon death as the dawning of a new life on a beautiful, final journey. When death strikes, they are not afraid, because they have prepared for it. They are aware that there is life after death, and they have made a choice as to where they will spend eternity. Two of my friends relive here their experiences in the loss of one of their children. They share their feelings about death, which, I pray, may be a source of great comfort to anyone who has suffered such a loss.

From the jungles of South American, in Pucallpa, Peru, two of my college classmates, Marge and Les Bancroft, returned after being there previously for thirty-four years before. This time Les's assignment was working on JAARS (Jungle Aviation and Radio Service) planes, filling in for the chief aviation mechanic who was on furlough. Marge filled various positions because of her many talents.

From their jungle home in Amazonia, Marge shared an article with me about suffering when death struck her family. She said she had very little physical suffering, but they have had emotional suffering. She wrote:

> It was Thanksgiving morning in 1983. We were home from Papua, New Guinea, and living in our home at the Wycliffe JAARS Center in Waxhaw, North Carolina. Our son, Brad, and his family were coming to have dinner with us, so I was up early and had the turkey in the oven. Les and I were lingering at the breakfast table with a second cup of coffee when there was a knock on our front door. As I opened the front door, there stood Brad's father-in-law and one of Brad's best friends. They walked in, looked at Les and me (Myles, our youngest son, was still in bed), and then they blurted out those words that changed not only our day, but also our lives.
>
> "Brad is dead," they said in unison. We had a hard time absorbing their words. Myles came bounding out into the living room in tears and sat down on the sofa beside Les, who also was crying. *What is the matter with me?* I thought. *I'm not crying.* I'm usually very emotional, but I had no tears. I had the feeling that the Lord had wrapped his arms round me and kept saying, *Marge, I've answered all of your prayers.* You see, for over two years, I had prayed daily, sometimes many times a day, "Lord, do anything you have to do to bring Brad back into fellowship with you, and when you do, I want it to be permanent."
>
> As my mind raced to all of the things I had to do, I felt like I had a never-ending recording playing through my brain, *In every thing give thanks: for this is the will of God in Christ Jesus* (1 Thess. 5:18a KJV). I began phoning family, pastors, and supporters around the country. Our co-laborers at Waxhaw began gathering at our house. I turned off the turkey and felt we needed to

get to Brad's house where his wife, Kathy, and sixteen-month-old daughter, Kelli, were going through the same shock.

Hundreds of people came to the funeral home, and I never saw so many grown men, all business friends of Brad, crying openly. He was manager of a local airport and was well-known in the area. The day of the funeral was beautiful. The sky was Carolina blue with buttermilk-white clouds. As we came out of the small chapel at the cemetery, I saw four airplanes coming from a distance, and they flew directly overhead. They were piloted by his pilot friends in their small private planes. As they got overhead, one of the small planes dipped its wing, broke formation and flew off in another direction—all alone.

I heard a loud sob, and as Myles and one of Brad's closest business associates grabbed me, I realized the sob was my own. Brad had really gone on to glory without the rest of us. It was several days later when the flood of tears broke for me, and I was able to release my pent-up emotions. I found it hard to sleep at night, and I would get up in the dark and sit alone in the living room and review Brad's life from the time I knew we were to have him until the day of his death. Through this exercise, the Lord gave me real assurance that Brad was "home with the Lord," even though he had been drifting away because of his pressing business.

In many ways the Lord allowed us to piece together the night of his death, but never really a reason why his car went over a steep embankment as he drove home from work alone. Kathy worked in the hospital emergency room until 11 P.M. She arrived home and saw that Brad wasn't home from the airport, so she picked Kelli up at the baby sitter. She thought about phoning the airport to tell Brad that she and the baby were home, but she thought it would make him climb down to answer the phone. He was working late in his shop on a Bell helicopter from Canada, and he was racing to get it finished.

I knew the Lord had everything in place. If he had been found the night of the accident, they would have taken him to the emergency room where Kathy worked. If he had picked up Kelli before it happened, she could have been strapped in her car seat alone in the rain all night. He was just within a mile of the baby sitter when his life came to a sudden end. I knew the

Lord hadn't made a mistake. I kept saying over and over, "Lord, I don't understand, but I trust You."

Now it is eleven years later, and I can say with the apostle Paul in 2 Corinthians 1:3–4, "Praise be to the God and Father of our Lord Jesus Christ, the Father of compassion and the God of all comfort, who comforts us in all our troubles, so that we can comfort those in any trouble with the comfort we ourselves have received from God" (NIV).

—*Marge Bancroft, Pucallpa, Peru, and Waxhaw, North Carolina*

Death can strike anywhere, anytime, to anybody. Often there are no warnings. Many lives are affected and changed because of the loss of a loved one; it may also mellow the hardest of hearts. Many times the pastor's funeral message and scripture will change a life.

Fictitious names are used in the next tragedy because my dear friend wanted to protect the family of the guilty person who killed her daughter—by accident. It was extremely difficult for "Mary" to talk about that day, but for the first time, she told me the following painful experience:

On a Saturday morning fourteen years ago, Betty, my twenty-nine-year-old daughter, her husband, Jim, and Joy, my six-year-old granddaughter, were involved in a traffic accident that claimed the life of my only daughter.

Jim saw that a car was not slowing for the red light, then he screamed for Betty to grab Joy. Within seconds, their van was on its side, against a curb. Betty and Joy had been thrown from the front seat and were both trapped by the van. "Don't cry Daddy, I'll be all right," Joy told her dad, as emergency workers struggled to free her from the door of the van. Her dad was only slightly injured; he and passersby attempted to lift the weight of the van from its victims. Joy was freed only after the fire department cut through the wreckage. Her little legs were placed in splints, and she was transported to a local hospital.

"She was the bravest six-year-old I've ever seen," the emergency medical technician said to the news reporter. "She never cried." Everyone marveled at her bravery, but emergency crews could not get to Betty. Wooden crates were used to lift the van from the crushed body of my daughter. Authorities said she apparently was killed instantly. I can only thank God that she did not suffer, and that she did not lie in agony under the van. A nurse friend of Betty's lived a short distance from the accident. She went immediately to the scene and called me as quickly as possible, saying only, "Joy is OK." The shock of the news left me frozen. Then fear grabbed my heart, as I wondered about the condition of the others.

My husband went immediately to the hospital; he wanted me to stay home with Mama and Daddy. I stayed, but I remained in constant prayer that our daughter would be all right. Then the call came. In a trembling voice, my husband said that he had identified the body of Betty. His words cut through my heart with a piercing throb! We were overwhelmed with grief. Oh, that feeling of utter helplessness and that aching void that no one can understand except those who have experienced such shock and immediate loss.

Joy's condition necessitated her being transferred to a hospital ninety miles away. Betty's nurse friend went with Joy in the ambulance. It tore our hearts to see our precious granddaughter go without us. But we had to make our daughter's funeral arrangements.

In the ambulance, Joy asked the nurse, "Where is Mommy?" The nurse told her that Mommy had gone to heaven. She and Joy cried and talked about her mommy—all the things her mommy had done for Joy and the happy times they had had together.

Our church members and many friends brought food to express their love and sympathy.

A few weeks after this tragic accident, our new pastor was driving behind his wife's car. His mother-in-law and their little French poodle were with his wife. As he watched helplessly, he saw a car hit his wife's car, killing all of them—in a twinkle of an eye. He came to us. He, too, was experiencing the stabbing pain of his great loss. We could understandably comfort each other. There is a bond that draws people together when they travel the same road of this indescribable pain.

For nine months, Joy was in a cast from her shoulders to her toes. A little boy wanted to do something special for his friend, Joy. Christmas was coming, and he knew Joy had no mother to be with her during the holidays. This thoughtful little boy wrote to Santa: "Dear Santa, I want you to bring something special to my friend, Joy, who was in a car accident and lost her mother. . . ." His letter was printed in the local newspaper with letters to Santa from other youngsters. He wanted to buy a doll that his family could not afford. Two days later, after his letter was printed in the paper, he got a letter with no return address. Inside was a note signed "From Santa's helper," and cash was enclosed for the exact cost of the doll he wanted to buy for Joy. This precious boy was only one of many generous people who touched our hearts. God works through others as His instruments to bring cheer and joy to His children. God works in mysterious ways, His wonders to perform!

Joy's bad leg was broken again in a bicycle accident, which necessitated a brace with screws, but today she walks as normally as any other person.

My thoughts go back to the day my daughter was born and the horrible pain of childbirth. However, the sudden-death pain I experienced in the loss of my only daughter cannot be put into words. At age twenty-nine, she was snatched away from me by a man who drove through a red light because he was looking at flowers along the way. He was not injured, but my daughter was killed.

Several years before Betty died, she called me wanting to know how she could be sure she was a Christian. I told her, using the plan of salvation, that she needed to ask Jesus to forgive her of her sins and to believe that God raised Him from the dead and she would be saved, and for her to read this in Romans 10:9–10. What a blessed, comforting, and joyful truth to know that someday I will be with her in heaven! "The Lord gave and the Lord has taken away. Blessed be the name of the Lord" (Job 1:21b NASB).

—"Mary", Mississippi

King Solomon sought to know the pleasures of life. He learned the realities of life and the philosophy, and he said, "I have seen all the things that are done under the sun; all of them are meaningless, a chasing after the wind" (Eccles. 1:14 NIV).

We are physically born in this earth only once and man is destined to die only once. What then? The Bible says, "And inasmuch as it is appointed for men to die once and after this comes judgment" (Heb. 9:27 NASB).

For me, I know that death will be the shedding of this earthly, deteriorated body, and my spirit will be released to enter into the presence of my Lord, where I shall dwell forever and ever.

In heaven, there are no tears, no sorrow, no death, no *pain*. Praise God, I have that blessed hope and assurance of beholding the magnificent glory of my God! My prayer is for every reader to have this assurance!

Chapter Nine

Profound Experiences

O ne of the hardest things for any individual or family is to have a loved one moved in to a nursing home. When a husband and wife can go together, they seem to adjust better. But when one goes alone, especially after the death of the other, it is more difficult. A distinguished man reflects his suffering from such a problem, while another friend shows the dissimilarity in depending on doctors, and depending on constant prayer *and* doctors in handling her problem with migraine headaches and myositis. A third person suffered ten years with excruciating stomach pains until she met a "singing surgeon" who diagnosed her with a diseased gall bladder that was full of stones. And a fourth friend's injury caused a deformed body, but her vision of Christ during a painful time was an indelible experience. It is uplifting to see how these Christians handled their situations.

When asked to think about one's most painful experience, some of us may not want to reminisce. A special person, Dr. Johnny V. Miller, President, Columbia International University, was intrigued by my question. One of his statements revealed his strong feelings about the subject: "Your question has caused me to reflect a lot in the last several days. One thing that I have realized in the past is that what some people consider painful has *not* been that way for Jeanne and me. We both came from challenging backgrounds, so there are lots of circumstances that we take in stride that others seem to find devastating."

The above resolution reiterates my conjecture that pain has a wide coverage, involves others, and in some instances, numerous individuals. Then Dr. Miller gave five short synopses, with "the most painful episode" too personal for publication. He revealed his character when he stated it would be impossible to cause pain or harm to a friend or others. As Dr. Miller said in his letter, "As I've tried to reflect on painful experiences, all of the real pain has come through relationships, most of them vicariously, as I was a pastor and missionary. Here is one that is personal and intimate, yet not too intimate to share":

One of the most painful experiences I have ever had was when I put my father into a nursing home. In his early sixties, he had become partially paralyzed due to a stroke, but he was able to live with my mother, who was not strong, and the two seemed to manage well. They lived just a couple of blocks from my older sister and her family in Port Arthur, Texas.

However, several years after my mother died, my father weakened to the point that he could not live alone. This became evident when he fell one day in his bathroom and lay on the floor for eighteen hours before a neighbor found him and called the family. I was pastoring a church in a Houston suburb, so we asked my father to come live with us. He was stubbornly independent, but we pled, and finally "soft talked" him into it, even though for him it meant selling his house and giving up his independence.

It was soon apparent to us that his mind and emotions were weakening along with his body. He had suffered from hardening of the arteries for several years. Toward the end of the first year that he lived with us, the Lord redirected our lives. I accepted the opportunity to teach at Columbia Bible College. We searched for an affordable house large enough for our extended family, and then began the process of trying to convince my father to move to South Carolina with us. He was adamant that he was going to move back to Arizona, where he had worked during most of his career, and was going to take care of himself. He angrily opposed moving to South Carolina. He would go West, or nowhere.

By this time, he could barely walk by himself with the help of a walker and needed help dressing, sitting, and rising. He daily spent long stretches fantasizing about recapturing his independence. He was sure that if he could return West, he would find his friends and his health. We struggled with what to do. Whenever we mentioned the move, he became angry. He assured us that he wanted us to go, believing it was God's will for us. But just as dogmatically, he swore that he would not go and we could not make him.

When we told him that, realistically, there was only one other option—to move into a nursing home—he declared that it was better than having to move east, instead of west, from Texas. I can still smell and feel what it was like the day that we moved him and his few allowed belongings into the nursing home. All my life I had declared that I would take care of my parents. Now I was overwhelmed with a sense of guilt and failure. *How could I leave my own father in a nursing home? Who would understand? How was he going to cope being without his family? Who would understand him?*

We left him in July, visited once in the fall, and again in December. He had always been a very large man, but he began losing weight immediately. By the time we saw him in December, he was almost 100 pounds lighter. He died of a stroke three days after Christmas. I still wonder if the problem that conquered him was depression over being left in the home. He never complained to me about it. His mind seemed very fuzzy thereafter. Was he already on that downward slide? Was it exacerbated by his circumstances? Or was he experiencing the consequences of anger that he had held and the willful choices he had made all of his life that finally culminated in his being so alone at the end?

—*Dr. Johnny V. Miller, President, Columbia International University, Columbia, South Carolina*

Dr. Miller's anguish is expressed in his deep-seated words flowing from a love for his father. He did what he knew was best for him. I am sure Dr. Miller bathed the situation with prayer and waited on the Lord for His guidance.

This is a problem facing many families today. The regular visits of a family member to a nursing home is vital to assure proper care. How often I have seen lonely nursing home residents sitting, longing to see a familiar face. If you don't have a loved one in a nursing home, you can bring happiness to one whose family never visits; an aide can introduce you to such a person. The Lord would be well pleased for you to adopt such a person to whom you can give some love and attention. An occasional small gift of personal needs, a cheerful flower, figurine, picture, or a short ride would make that lonely one so happy.

One of my college classmates has remained a close friend throughout the years. She has shared the following about her battle with migraine headaches and myositis and the power of prayer:

Two of my most painful experiences and what made the difference: As a child, I remember having headaches. In my late teens, I was diagnosed with migraine headaches. Eventually, a medicine was prescribed to prevent them.

When I was nearly fifty years old, I experienced the worst headaches in my life, worse than any migraine. My doctor put me in the hospital on the pretense of measuring my legs to see if they were the same length; but instead he put traction on my neck with a five-pound weight. Immediately, I had a terrible pain in my head. The pain became so intense that my husband had the traction stopped.

After I was released from the hospital, the headaches started in the back of my head when I went to sleep at night. They were excruciating! The only thing I could do was sit up in bed and cry. I tried to sleep, but no medication worked. Finally I was sent to a world-renowned neurologist, who found nothing abnormal. He said that the headaches would disappear after a year. This is exactly what happened. The last of those headaches was so bad that I just sat in bed praying for morning to come. I had depended on the doctor to help me, but praise the Lord, He heard and answered my prayers! All things are possible with Him!

Another excruciatingly painful experience happened twenty years later. Thank God, that one lasted only about a month. I was cleaning one day and stretched the muscles in my left arm and shoulder, which brought on a recurrence of myositis, which I had had in other muscles. Medicine takes time to take effect on this disease. Most of the night I had to sit in a chair, as it was too painful to lie down in any position. This time I called my pastor who is a strong believer in the power of prayer. He prayed and also asked our Sunday School class and the church to pray for me. As soon as they started praying for me, I began to be able to sleep in my bed.

The difference between these two experiences is obvious. In the first painful experience, I was depending on doctors to heal me; but the second time, I knew that *primary healing comes from God.* I depended on Him to hear our prayers and to heal me—through the cooperation of medications and doctors. I am now seventy-three years of age, and I know it is God who does the healing. I've claimed Psalm 40:1: "I waited patiently for God to help me; then he listened and heard my cry" (TLB). I believed; we prayed; He answered our prayers! I know He is all powerful!
—*Mrs. Evelyn Armstrong Dudney, Warner Robins, Georgia*

Less than a year before I began writing this book, God brought Mary Palmer into my life. At the time, I urgently needed a compassionate sitter for a dear friend of mine who had had emergency surgery. Mrs. Desma Blanks, a friend, resided at a nursing home, and I was her attorney-in-fact, responsible for all medical, legal, and other decisions. It was during my frequent visits to this nursing home that I learned the needs of so many of the residents.

Desma was different because she is a self-sufficient person. During a serious illness and surgery, Mary Palmer was recommended as an excellent bed-sitter. She brought joy and comfort to Mrs. Blanks for many months. She proved to be a friend and companion to Mrs. Blanks, which is vital in helping a person recover. When Mary learned I was working on this book, she shared the following story:

For almost ten years I had acute, excruciating pains in my stomach. The doctors in Michigan, where I lived then, could never diagnose my problem. About three or four times a year, I was taken to the emergency room because of the acute, sharp, cutting pain that had me almost bent double. I was given pain medications, but no diagnosis.

Later, I moved to Mississippi. When I had one of those acute attacks, a doctor in the emergency department discovered that I had gall stones and a diseased gall bladder. Surgery by a well-known surgeon in my city found stones in the duct tube, and he removed my gall bladder. Dr. James C. Matthews, Jr., known as the "singing surgeon," found many small, black stones in my gall bladder, which he put in a small sandwich bag for me to see. What a relief to know I would *never* have those horrible attacks again! He saved my life!

Thank God for doctors who can help, and have compassion and understanding for their patients! I was free of pain, and I have no fear of ever having those torturous pains again! During all those painful attacks, I had faith in God. I knew He would get me through those ordeals. God was with me then; He is with me at all times now. I know that He loves and cares for me. Praise His holy name! I give Him all the praise!

—*Mary L. Palmer, Meridian, Mississippi*

Illnesses at any age can change one's way of life. But to have an injury and not be able to get medical help can affect one's future. I was not aware of a prior neighbor's physical suffering from a fall, and her vision of Christ during that painful time, until she sent the following story to me:

Crash! A broken limb and I was lying unconscious on the ground under a cherry tree from which I had been picking cherries. I was twelve years of age, very small for my age. I felt sure the old limbs would hold my tiny frame of 52 pounds. The misjudgment caused me a deformed body and much pain during my lifetime.

Because my family could not afford to place me in a hospital, I was taken care of at home. My internal bleeding was treated with ice packs on my right side to help deaden the pain. During one of those painful times, I was suddenly aware of a vision of Christ standing at the foot of my bed. His robe was a flash of soft white, and His face and eyes were so soft, gentle, sympathetic, and loving. I have never forgotten His wonderful face. His eyes were a soft brown, more expressive than any human eye. They seemed to "speak" a thousand words, yet He did not speak a word. As I looked at Him with both fright and wonder, the pain completely left me; I felt like I was in a true utopia, perfectly attuned to His wonderful self. I had an overpowering feeling of love and goodness. I think I felt the peace and light of heaven. It was so grand that to this day, I have *no* fear of death.

The following morning, I heard my doctor tell my mother that he had thought I would never make it through the night, but that I seemed much improved. He was actually shocked at such a sudden turn for the better of my serious condition. The pain was less, and I had had this wonderful visit from God in my heart that helped me bear the pain.

I have never since experienced the perfect peace, contentment, and sheer joy that filled me during this unique, miraculous experience when pain suddenly left me. I know the Lord was with me; I experienced His presence. He touched me and healed me. I am now seventy-two and have arthritis on the injured side, but I thank God that He visited me as a twelve-year-old girl when I was in such agony. Only He brought me through such a painful ordeal. I know that He walks and talks with me today. What joy, peace, and hope fills my soul to know that He will never leave me.

As I think back on this experience that happened many years ago, I am comforted by the words that Moses spoke to the children of Israel: "The Lord himself goes before you and will be with you; he will never leave you nor forsake you. Do not be afraid; do not be discouraged" (Deut. 31:8 NIV).

—*Mrs. Irene N. Colen, Gulf Shores, Alabama*

These profound experiences all prove the power of prayer. Jesus said, "If you believe, you will receive whatever you ask for in prayer" (Matt. 21:22 NIV).

Some people in nursing homes are suffering tremendously from physical and emotional problems at this moment. Children are injured from accidents throughout the day, and physical illnesses are creating undue stress throughout our world. We are our Lord's instruments, who can be used to help in many painful situations.

When we are in tune with Him, we will know what we can do to help those in need. This is where the love of God is shown by expressing His love in action and by being constant in prayer with Him; His Spirit reveals to us what He would have us do. Thank God for His abiding presence to guide and direct our lives in our everyday activities.

Chapter Ten

Spiritual Crossroads

A beautiful city, Indianapolis, Indiana, is sometimes called the "Crossroads of America." Indianapolis is intersected by more segments of interstate highway than any other metropolitan area, according to The Indianapolis Project fact sheet. With the many routes of highways and railroad traffic meeting in this one city, it could easily become a hazard. However, the dependable, alert employees in all work areas of this amazing transportation center reveal the awareness of each person's responsibility and also the responsibilities of their co-workers. They are closely attuned to their accountability to each other in saving lives and avoiding confusion and any disorder.

In our travels, none of us enjoys being helpless at crossroads. If a passage way is unmarked, unknown, or blocked, we usually take the road that appears to be the main thoroughfare. Often in the spiritual arena, we come to crossroads. It may be a trial-and-error, wait-and-see, or an unusual "eureka" experience. When one thinks "I found it!" and then becomes disappointed or disenchanted, serious consequences usually develop. This arena refers specifically to a group of people who gather to worship for the purpose of satisfying the inborn hunger and thirst of a restless spirit.

That inner turmoil and longing desire to worship a supreme being has found people worshipping the sun, hand-carved idols, animals, or whatever their ancestors worshipped, until they discovered that there is an eternal Jehovah God. Only then can true peace flood a human being's soul. Happiness is fulfilled when a gathering of sincere people work in unity to satisfy their longing souls. When church flare-ups glow, crossroads often appear.

Crossroads Lead to Decision-Making Experiences

One person, a dear friend called "Rebecca," has now written about, her experiences, which describe all aspects of pain through deep, heart-rending ordeals. She revealed the hurt that pastors and church members caused by their words and actions in three different churches. Opening her heart so honestly may challenge professing Christians to wake up and see if the searchlight reveals "Thou art the man!" as Nathan told David in a very dramatic story in the Bible in 2 Samuel 12:7. Rebecca wrote:

> Throughout my lifetime, I have experienced several types of pain. I have had physical pain from childbirth, car accidents, and other happenings that I have been involved in, and I suffered greatly. I have also had emotional pain, and sometimes this is the worst. I believe it happens with all types of pain, whether it is physical or spiritual: Our emotions are affected. Spiritual pain seems to last the longest. I think for me, the pain that I remember the most, and that has lasted the longest, has been spiritual pain.
>
> This started many years ago when I went to work for a preacher. I was so excited and felt that this would be such a good experience for me and would draw me closer to God. But this did not happen. In fact, it took about three months to learn that this "man of God" was not on a pedestal, where I had put all preachers. This so-called man of God smoked and could curse worse than any sailor I had ever been around during our Navy days.
>
> I began to question a lot of things as a result of this professing Christian, a pastor, who was actually a spiritual stumbling block to me. I became very uneasy around him. I was thankful when we moved and changed churches. It was at this church

that I talked with my new pastor about my previous church problem. My pain was easing some, but then I heard that the congregation wanted to get rid of this pastor. The year of turmoil in our new church tore at my faith and heart until I wondered if "religion" was really worth it. Because of my children, I hid this pain, disappointment, and discouragement.

Another move took us to a new state, a new community, and a new church. After ten months, I was beginning to have a great renewal of faith and my doubts were leaving. This church helped heal the spiritual pain that I had felt for five years. But it just didn't last long enough for me to really get on solid ground after going through such an unhappy, shaky experience.

Another job promotion for my husband took us farther north, closer to my aging parents. Once again, the search for a new church was on for me and my family. After a few weeks, we found a church with a great youth program for our teenage daughter. Everything seemed to be going great; my faith was healing, and I was beginning to trust people again. Then we heard rumors that some of the members wanted the pastor to leave. They complained because he didn't visit as they thought he should, he didn't go where they wanted him to go, and worst of all, he disagreed with the deacons! It sounded to me as if they wanted a puppet, or maybe a follower of them, and not God's spokesman and leader. This was very disenchanting to me and my family!

The youth department had grown from ten to ninety-seven teenagers within three years. But many adults complained that too much money was spent on the youth program. It was like the other church I mentioned; the church members fighting with harsh words, disgruntled, and not getting along with each other. The church was divided with people taking sides on certain issues.

One Sunday, all the deacons made a big public appeal to the people to come together and back the pastor. They asked that the people pray. I really felt good about this. Then all of a sudden—BOOM!—we were shocked at a sudden turn. The deacons met only three days after making their big public appeal, and *they* decided to let the pastor go. Needless to say, the next Sunday when the deacons made their announcement during the worship service, shock rippled throughout the congregation. So once again, I felt betrayed by other Christians.

By then my children were grown and on their own, but I had lost that burning desire to attend church again. For three years I went to church only when I visited my parents and sister. I even arranged my work schedule so that I worked on Sundays and had an excuse not to be available for church attendance because the pain was still deep within! I knew I needed to be in a church, but the pain of being afraid to trust church people had been a time of turmoil and agony for me. I kept very private about my feelings as I did not want to influence anyone by my negative attitude.

Within, I had a deep longing to worship in a loving church with the expected Christian fellowship. I had become discouraged with my denomination through all these experiences, and I began attending other churches of several different denominations. I was looking for an answer to that deep, gnawing pain from the lack of worshipping in a church with others of like mind as I had in my younger, happier, churchgoing days.

In writing this experience, I have felt some healing. In fact, I have realized that I was just using excuses to feel sorry for myself. I have been needing to deal with all of this in a positive way to help make me stronger and look to God, not at weak, immature, churchgoing, Bible-toting, professing Christians. In moving into a new home in a new community, I discovered a church about one-half mile from our home.

I have learned that I can not let people be my deciding factor in my faith and my worship. My faith is in Jesus Christ because He is always the same, and He never fails. I remember from a Bible study that the middle verse in the Bible is Psalm 118:8: "It is better to trust in the Lord than to put confidence in man" (KJV). Now my goal is always to keep this in mind: God is really the *only* person I can trust! I am resolved that I will not let the past be a spiritual threat to my life by trusting in man. I have learned that spiritual pain is also emotional pain and physical pain all rolled into one. What a relief and a joy to learn that only Jesus can solve every problem.

—*"Rebecca" in South Carolina*

Rebecca's story is too common in many churches today. Newcomers to a church can be hindered in their Christian walk by pious, bench-warming church members. She was deeply hurt by such people, but her mistake was in looking at unstable, professing Christians instead of God.

Her eyes were opened; her heart is now changed, and she seeks to worship with a God-fearing, humble, Christ-centered, Bible-teaching church. How distressing that today such a church can be hard to find!

May God keep us from spiritually hindering others as Rebecca has been. This kind of pain affected her not only spiritually, but also physically and emotionally. But God is faithful; let us trust Him, not people. We have heard the expression that some people have "jellyfish spines," and as time passes, it seems that more and more I am meeting such people.

In the greatest country in the world we have doors of opportunity opening to help those in need. The need may be in our own homes, our neighbors, community, or churches. Yet the opportunity slips through our fingers because we don't want to get involved, or it may entail too much time away from our personal interests. When it comes to our churches, we often sit back and think someone else can do the job.

We also are prone to judge and misjudge, forgetting that the purpose of going to church is to *worship*. Sometimes churchgoing may become a social outlet, with a clique ruling, or trying to rule, a church. This scenario becomes too prevalent in churches when they don't use the Word of God as the source of guidance.

The following painful story is described by a person, who asked to be called "Roy," and he tells about what he calls spiritual pain among God's people.

> The most crucial pain that I have ever felt was inflicted on me by God's people. To help you understand the magnitude of the hurt, I will tell you part of the events of my life leading up to the time in question. I was raised in a Christian home in rural Mississippi. My parents had me in church every Sunday. We often went in a wagon pulled by a tractor or team of mules, but we went.
>
> Life went along normally for young boys living in a rural area like ours. At least they did for me until at age seven; I was

sexually molested by older boys in my community. I was never able to tell my parents of the incident because of the shame and guilt that I felt. Because of that incident, I never could be friends with those boys, or with any other males later in my life. I was totally confused about who I was and what my purpose in life was. I was a very depressed person, so depressed in fact, that I often entertained thoughts of suicide. No one knew what was going on in my life, just that I was always in trouble and difficult to understand.

Trying to prove my manhood, I started using pornographic material that had been given to me by an older man in our community. Later, I came to realize that this was not helping me but had established a stronghold in my life that I could not change. I went to church with my family and pretended that everything was all right. I even joined the church, hoping that this would bring some relief. Still, life went on and nothing seemed to help.

At age eighteen, I left home with a boy who was also running from his family, and himself. We went to Tampa, Florida, to attend trade school. Soon, the young man I had gone with dropped out of school and joined the Army. This left me again without anyone to call a friend. I continued my life of pornography addiction, thoughts of suicide, depression, and rejection.

I soon met a woman who had a lot of the same problems that I had. (It's amazing how birds of a feather flock together.) We soon became sexually active. This type of relationship only added to the confusion already present. The chain of events that caused me to leave home only compounded as life went on. My parents did not approve of the relationship that I had with this young woman, so I married her to show my parents that I could do things for myself.

I graduated from trade school and we moved back to my hometown, only to be drafted into the Army. After training, I was sent to Vietnam for a twelve-month tour. Six months later, I was wounded and sent home to convalesce. When I was well again, my wife and I were stationed at Fort Carson, Colorado.

After two years, the marriage started to fall apart, and we were soon divorced. Still, no real friend had been found. I actively used drugs and alcohol to try to ease the pain of being friendless. Seeking companionship, I married a local girl, fresh out of high school. Within a year, we had a son. Things seemed to be going fine, but underneath, the tide of defeat was doing its damage. I did not understand why, but the harder times became, the more I wanted to go back home.

After seven years of military life, I got out of the Army and moved my family back to my hometown. Once again, the memories of the past haunted me night and day, keeping me captivated by a lifestyle of depression, alcohol, pornography, and defeat.

My desire for approval from my family and friends, caused me to live a life of Jekyll and Hyde to those who knew me. When I was with one group, I would act the way they expected; the same would be true when I was with the other group. I moved my family from place to place, trying to find that perfect spot to live, hoping that this would bring about the necessary changes that were needed in my life. But misery, discontent, and fatigue were taking their toll. I had changed jobs several times, always seeming to improve my lifestyle. But this brought about even more confusion.

A second child, a girl, was born. Things seemed to improve for short periods of time, but each time I changed back to my old ways, and they were always worse than before. Finally, in 1983, I moved my family to our current residence in a small community in East Central Mississippi. The old house we bought needed much repair. But I had been blessed with several skills, and I had the drive to work hard. So with new life I plunged into remodeling this old house.

Shortly after moving in, a young man several years my junior (I'll call him "Sam") came uninvited to help me work on the roof of my house. This greatly impressed me. Someone I hardly knew just showed up and helped me with a job of magnitude. It started a friendship that is still alive today, and our common interest of hunting and fishing helped the friendship to grow over the first few years.

Still, the nagging history of my life kept me from being close to my wife and children. I tried to fill the gaps with alcohol and pornography. Working shifts at a paper mill in western Alabama allowed me to always have an excuse (a skin of a reason stuffed with a lie) to attend church irregularly. I managed to keep up my front with most of my family and friends. However, my wife and children knew me too well. Verbal abuse was regularly given by me. There seemed to be no out for me!

In 1987, the small Baptist church that we attended called a new pastor. This man was young and full of energy. Wanting the church to grow, he started a youth ministry, made plans for a revival, and started a discipleship program for the adults who wanted to grow. A summer youth camp was planned in Texas, and my wife volunteered to go. Our marriage was at its worst state, and she realized that something had to be done if it was to last. Little did she know that God had already been working in the heart of her husband. Upon her return from Texas with the youth, I noticed that she was not the same. The trip had changed a lot of people, including my wife. I recognized that she had a relationship that I did not have, a real love relationship with God.

I made an appointment with my pastor for Saturday afternoon. We met and when I later left the pastor's office, I had convinced him that I was saved, for I knew all the right answers. Still, within my own heart I knew that I was indeed lost. That Sunday was the start of a revival. I sang in the choir, helped "pack a pew," and even sat in the second row after the choir sang. The evangelist preached on relationships and said that if you were not properly related to God, you would spend eternity in a place called hell. At the end of the service, an invitation was given for people to respond and receive a relationship with God through His Son Jesus Christ. I could hardly wait to respond, for I now understood that the only relationship that really counted was my relationship to God.

That night I started down the road to victory! The pastor spent a lot of time with me to disciple me and my growth was very rapid. During my childhood, some old godly aunts had taught me in Sunday School, and to my amazement most of that teaching came back to me, fulfilling scripture that His word would not return void.

Things were improving on a steady basis, and by 1990, I was elected as a deacon in the church. This proved to be one of the toughest things that I had faced. When I first moved to the community, I had been told of a man who constantly argued and kept things in turmoil. The man was once a deacon in this church but had left to attend another church, only as a member.

I soon realized that things were not as they appeared to be in the church. Being a deacon exposed me to a lot of things that were not seen by most members of the church. This, I believe now, is very wrong, because it enables things to happen that should not happen.

For the most part, the church was led by three or four old church families and not by the Holy Spirit. This greatly confused me, because I had been taught differently. After several months of obvious conflict among the deacons, an incident occurred that proved to tear at the very fiber of my being. The man who could not get along with people, and who by now had returned to this church, had openly slandered a very godly lady in the church. Upon knowledge of this, the pastor and chairman of the deacons visited this man only to be *cursed* by him. When this was brought to the deacon body, it was ruled by a majority to place the incident aside and move on with the business at hand.

This action not only confused me, but also several other people who had been saved and discipled since the new pastor had come to the church. I soon became angry again and started to think like I had always thought. The months rolled by, with no one wishing to address the issues at hand. Finally, God moved the pastor to another town on the west side of the state. Wanting to remain and be a part of the solution, I began to work to resolve the differences.

In several deacon meetings, the above-named issue—as well as other issues of prejudices and open rebellion against God—were discussed. The deacon body steadfastly would not deal with the issues according to God's Word, but only with man's reasoning. Several people in the church moved to other churches where they could once again worship God. Pressure was applied to make those people conform to their way of thinking. When that did not work, open scorn was applied. This broke my heart, and I'm quite sure, the heart of God. Some people in the church desired an open confrontation with the deacon body, but I realized that this would probably cause a very ugly split in the church.

In a last chance move, I wrote a letter to the members of the church, stating the incidents and issues and pleading for us, the church, to deal with them biblically, which meant confession, repentance, and then restoration, to receive God's blessings. I ended my letter by saying that the Bible says that God is not the author of confusion, but of love, peace, and of a sound mind. (My combined translations of 1 Corinthians 14:33).

This letter was mailed or hand delivered to almost every member of the church. The results were almost unbearable. People who had said they were brothers and sisters in Christ would now not even speak. My family was ridiculed by almost everyone, including my supposed best friend, Sam.

My wife worked at Sam's business. and several other people from the church also worked there. My wife came home day after day, crying and telling me how difficult it was to work there with people she loved but who would not return that love. Instead, they said things to make her life as miserable as possible. Both our children were shunned by their previous friends. Anger soon turned to bitterness, especially for me. I had never had a close friend before this relationship, and that, too, was severed. I became angry at God for allowing this to happen. It was obvious by this time that some of God's people really know how to inflict pain on His people who do not think like they do.

My family received counsel from several pastors and family members who *would* talk to us. We found a loving and growing church nearby that welcomed us. To my amazement, things seemed to be different at this church. There was an open love that allowed the Spirit of God to minister to me and my family in a very real and personal way. Before long, the bitterness was confessed and repented of, and life seemed worth living again. The most important lesson for me in the whole experience has been this: That God is my very best friend. He will never leave me nor forsake me. He is our only true and lasting friend. Shortly after realizing this and giving my past relationships to God for healing, He restored several of those relationships.

Most of all, He restored the relationship of my physical family. He also restored the relationship of my best male friend outside my family. God is so good, faithful, righteous, holy, and just a good friend. So if you've been hampered, beat-up spiritually, abused, or just feel like you do not have a friend in the whole wide world, just simply look to God and He will fill you till "your cup runs over." Even if life and people treat us badly, God is always there to help us get through each and every problem.

Spiritual victory over this is great, and I look forward to future relationships, especially with God.

—*"Roy" in Mississippi*

The pain from spiritual conflicts within churches has cut deeply into the lives of many people. Some have not been able to physically, mentally, and emotionally stand up under the stress that has been experienced through a power struggle or a divisive battle in what is supposed to be God's house. Some churches have not been able to endure the skirmishes, and their doors have been closed permanently. Jesus, the Son of God, became so enraged with those who desecrated the house of God that He physically chased them out of the temple. If we, as God's instruments and ambassadors, permit God's holy temple to be stripped of His glory, I feel that we shall be judged accordingly. Our God is a holy God; we should enter into His presence with an attitude of adoration, humility, and holiness. The first Christians worshipped in a deep sense of awe; they met together regularly in a loving spirit of helping each other and sharing with those in need. They worshipped "with great joy and thankfulness, praising God" (Acts 2:46b–47a TLB).

We all come to spiritual crossroads, but when we focus our eyes, thoughts, and lives upon our awesome Lord, love will flood our souls and flow into the lives of others. We are the church. When people look at us, they are looking at representatives of that church. As we sometimes hear, "You may be the only Bible that some people will ever read."

May we be vibrant, committed, dedicated vessels for the Lord to work through to help others who reach those rough spiritual crossroads.

"But those who wait on the Lord shall renew their strength; They shall mount up with wings like eagles . . ." (Isa. 40:31*a* NKJV)

Chapter Eleven

The Challenge of Pain

~⁂~

In all stages of life, prenatal to death, we experience pain. Discomfort from any traumatic encounter may occur daily, occasionally, or even continuously for some of us. There are times when we may think, *I have had my share of suffering: why more?* But I doubt if we can really gauge suffering or measure it in any objective sense. Pain falls into varying degrees and in diverse areas of our lives. Each person handles pain of any kind differently. Some people come to accept pain as a challenge. Pain as a challenge? Do we let severe arthritis, diabetes, wheelchairs, or numerous other limitations stop us from all activities? Some of us don't!

When I was a child, I was shy. But when I became a surrendered Christian as a teenager, I was a bold, exuberant person, with challenges making me stronger. Beginning then, when anyone told me that I could *not* do something, that was the same as an injection of adrenaline. That seems to have been my life story. Pain has *never* conquered my spirited endeavors, but there have been slowdowns at times.

My mother told me that as an infant, I suffered agony during a serious bout with pneumonia combined with whooping cough; every breath, she thought, would be my last. Throughout my infancy,

I was sickly, but I always bounced back. My childhood was one filled with unusual illnesses, along with all the common childhood diseases. I frequently battled two problems at the same time.

Nevertheless, as a young child I became independent and never wanted pity, so my mother remarked. As I've grown older, it seems I have become an undaunted fighter, meeting everything with a confident spirit.

In grammar school, I was diagnosed with Bright's disease. Some memories are humiliating. Then, at times, my bouts with asthma and allergies were too much for my mother, so I stayed with my devoted grandmother, whom I called "Mama Charles." Our times together were not only influential, but also unforgettable. Later, rheumatic fever kept me in bed for weeks. When I returned to school, the annoyance of a fast-beating heart was frightening for fear of missing more school. Exercise caused a racing heart, short-windedness, and shakiness. Then at age thirteen, when my family moved from our rural southern community to Washington, DC, I was removed from my gym class because of my racing heart.

My youngest brother and I adjusted well in the big-city school, but fellow students constant pestering about my strong southern accent was provoking. My first day in school was embarrassing. When I was asked to give my name and other information, the whole class burst into laughter. I literally slid down low in my chair, with a burning, red face and wanted to run out of the room, never to return! One classmate made it her job to "teach" me how to talk. After every word spoken, she drilled me with the correct pronunciation. I started with my southern drawl, added to this a new way of speaking, and then a few years later had the strong exposure to a Bostonian accent. Is there any wonder of my strange dialect? Oh, yes, I have been accused of saying, "I paked my kah in the pakin lot."

Even though I had always been an extremely shy person, making friends seemed to come easily with some of my classmates, especially at my new church. Then a cruel and crude awakening brought me out of my timid shell. For adults to ask such shocking questions as "Had you ever tasted ice cream before you came to

Washington?" and "Did you have trouble learning to wear shoes?" Consequently, the shocks and rapid changes at that young age strengthened my self-confidence. But what a challenge!

The Beginning of a New Life

Accepting a friend's invitation, my younger brother and I went to her church, Fourth Presbyterian Church, our first Sunday in the big city. We continued going every Sunday without visiting other churches as we had planned. In fact, that venture was the beginning of a new life. One of my first remembrances of Fourth Church, as we called it, was the varied and well-planned youth programs. I was happier than I could ever remember!

One Sunday evening, the church's youth had a candlelight service. Each youth went to the front of the room and stood behind a table that displayed a tall, lit candle. As they humbly told what the Lord had done in their lives, overflowing joy touched my heart. When my turn came, I wasn't shy or frightened, but went boldly forward and shared as others had from the very depth of the heart. Prayerfully, I stood before my friends, took my candle, and said, "I have never had an experience like this before tonight. I remember joining a church when I was eight years old, but if I have never really asked the Lord Jesus to come into my heart, I do ask Him now. I want Him to have *complete* control of my life, and I thank Him for giving me friends who have helped me as you have."

Then I took my candle and held it to the tall, glowing one, slowly lighting my own. My dark candle suddenly changed into a beautiful, shining light. The first time in my life I felt free, like a bird out of a cage, overflowing with a joy unknown before.

That profound experience, along with the oneness in Christian fellowship with my friends, youth sponsor, and other church members, made a strong impact upon me. I shall never forget that moment! It was as if my life was *immediately* anchored into the depth of an unwavering stronghold. It was because I was anchored to the one and only Rock, my Lord and Savior Jesus Christ.

Suddenly, strength and courage to accept any challenge energized me, the little shy, country girl with the southern drawl. Since then I have had but one goal: to hold firmly to the commitment of letting the Lord have control of *everything* that touches my life, however traumatic. This complete turnabout was the marked beginning of a new person prepared to meet the demands for the future. Thank God, I did not know the future! It was then I chose my life verse: "I can do all things through Christ who strengthens me" (Phil. 4:13 NKJV). This verse has been a source of encouragement and strength throughout my life.

What a foundation was laid at that place of worship! Little did I know then that someday I would also become a member of the Hollywood Presbyterian Church, Hollywood, California, where Dr. Richard Halverson was one of the pastors. Later, he became a minister of Fourth Presbyterian Church in Washington, DC, where I had spent most of my teenage years. Then he became the sixtieth chaplain of the US Senate.

As years passed, another minister, Dr. Lloyd Ogilvie from Hollywood Presbyterian Church, followed in the distinguished footsteps of Dr. Halverson, becoming the sixty-first chaplain of the US Senate in March 1995. What a small world to have been members of both churches and to have known both spiritual leaders in my lifetime!

Challenging Teenage Years

Physically, life went fine until I was stricken with a severe case of strep throat. In my presence, the doctor said that I was dying and to rush me to the hospital. Mother said an emphatic, "No!" She said she knew I, her only daughter, would surely die in that hospital. Every word pierced my consciousness, but I was too weak to move any part of my body, even an eyelash. Mother was crying as she called my grandmother and others, appraising them of the serious situation. Mother and Dad helped save my life by flushing out what was called "green poison." The next day, the doctor called and asked mother if I was still alive. He had obtained a new drug, sulfa, which he had given a fourteen-year-old boy, but it was too late to save his life. But he rushed it to me, and within hours, a sudden change happened for the better.

Full recovery was a long hard road. I struggled and fought to regain strength. My summer was spent in Mississippi with my grandmother, Mama Charles, who was adamant about my eating hot, homemade cornbread soaked in broth produced by freshly cooked turnip greens.

Mama Charles said, and I have confirmed, that this food is an excellent source of iron and vitamins. That summer was the road to recovery of my health and strength. Upon returning to Washington, DC, I plunged into my schoolwork. I was thrilled that my teachers had graded me on past performance and my grades prior to becoming ill near the end of that last semester. In a class of 463 students at Central High School, I finished in the top thirteen in spite of missing my junior-year exams. But I worked hard and know now that I had been given an excellent foundation in my little country school in Mississippi by unusually dedicated teachers in my grammar school years.

An Exciting and Challenging Youth

My dream of working at the Department of State was an exciting goal. There was one problem; I was only seventeen and one had to be eighteen to work for the US government. My pastor at Fourth Church discovered my predicament, and a church decision was made to send me to business school until I became eighteen. But when mother heard that I was remaining in Washington, she *demanded* that I come home. My balloon had burst! Tears were shed, but I knew my mother! Millions of memories flooded my mind! I did not want to return home! My heart was torn and my emotions were mixed. My plans were all put on hold.

I had learned that God was in control of my life in spite of this head-on challenge. First thing on my agenda was a good paying job for my trip to DC after my November birthday. The problem was no job experience. My first job was as a typist with a reputable lawyer, and then I had a better paying job with a well-known insurance company in Meridian. Every available penny went to the bank. My plans were my secret, except for a few co-workers who knew. So when I took my first leave for a DC trip, they were surprised when I returned. However, my plans were finalized with the Department of State, and I only needed the official notification date to report to work.

What happy memories I have of those youthful, exciting days! Nothing dimmed my hope and goals. One of the happiest days of my life was my return trip to DC and settling down in my new job in the State Department. I went from typist, to secretary in the personnel department, then to an exiting job as the authentication clerk where I met many interesting diplomats.

Then one morning, I was standing in a crowded streetcar holding onto the upper handhold in the middle of the aisle. Suddenly, my heart took off like a race horse!

Later, I felt lightheaded and went to the State Department's nurse. After her treatment, my heartbeat was still over 180, so she sent me to my doctor. According to him, the medication she gave me was the "same as pouring gasoline on fire"—a stimulant that I didn't need. He gave me medication and sent me home with orders to "be quiet and rest."

Within a few months, he admitted me to the hospital because of fever and painful limbs. Before the test results were available, they admitted a suspicion of polio, which was new and rather rampant at that time. I was frightened! I prayed all night!

Little did I sleep, for I was bothered about a promise I had made to the Lord but had pushed aside. I had been having such a good time with my friends that I forgot my vow. I had promised the Lord, in front of my church friends, that I would go to Bible college to prepare as a missionary to Egypt. But I had not saved any money as planned and college expenses would be my responsibility. The next morning, a smiling doctor told me that polio was not my problem but rather a recurrence of rheumatic fever, which I had had as a child.

The relief was so great that I only remembered my all-night pleading with God: "Lord, please don't let me have polio. I promise to resign *as soon as* I return to work and make preparations to go to Bible college." My words were definite, concrete, and specific, and I was afraid to go back on my promise to God. This time

I was going to keep my oath! Previously, procrastination had been my problem. The Lord had to awaken me so there would be no flinching! My resignation was handed in my first day back at work and shock was written over the faces of my co-workers and boss.

Two Challenges and Two Choices

Then came the offer of a job in Foreign Service. With all the wonderful benefits, it was very, very tempting! The good salary, the countries I could visit, and other exciting "fringes" were like carrots held in front of a rabbit. After all, as a typical, young American girl, I did some realistic thinking. What a challenge! But why now? Why did they wait until I turned in my resignation? Traveling sounded great, but it was college now or probably never!

No, my mind was fixed! It was a "walk of faith," as I had no financial backing for college. The day my college acceptance papers arrived, I was ecstatic; they wanted me to start in January, the beginning of the second semester. And I had the offer of a job! The dean of women was impressed by my typed cover letter sent with my application and offered me a job as her part-time secretary. What an answer to prayer! My faith had been tested and then strengthened.

My college days were one challenge after another. Financially, I lived on a shoestring and the packages from my mother were gratefully accepted. In those days, a bar of soap, toothpaste, chewing gum, candy, cookies—anything—was a tremendous help. Every summer, a job became available. I marveled how the Lord met every need consistently!

During this time, I had to finish in three and a half years or I wouldn't have sufficient funds to return for graduation. Thus, I went to summer school, worked, and also registered for a Saturday class in my senior year—all in addition to a jammed schedule the entire year. I forgot the doctor's warning about taking life in its stride, getting the proper rest, and not pushing my body to a point of exhaustion.

My determination to get my college degree at the end of my third year meant cramming an additional semester into my last year. Thus, I would finish in three and one-half years with my classmates. During that time, an allergy problem had worsened and necessitated a doctor's visit. Nose drops were prescribed for severe nasal congestion and the usual allergy irritations.

For many months, I had been interested in an outstanding young man, and we had been dating as much as our school time permitted. This charming, inspiring person helped keep me going. His strong faith was a great encouragement.

Then attacks of tachycardia, the rapid heart problem that first occurred in DC, started again. This became a matter of concern because of that usual accompanying problem of lightheadedness and weakness. The college physician's orders were to use the elevator instead of the stairs. Eventually my "assignment" was to stay in the infirmary every weekend for complete rest.

My condition steadily worsened. My physician told me that I could not continue my last semester and should return home. I insisted on staying and asked for a schedule to keep up with my classes. His remark was stern: "If you stay here, I will accept *no* responsibility." I told him that the responsibility would be solely mine, for I knew that if I left I would never be financially able to return for my final semester. Then he told me something that was the same as throwing a bucket of cold water in my face. He slowly and compassionately said, "You will never be able to work. If you marry and become pregnant, you won't live through childbearing. You have a 'veteran's heart.'" I wondered, *What is a veteran's heart?* He continued, "You will not be able to give your required chapel message."

I momentarily erased everything he had said, except that last statement. The chapel message was essential for graduation, and I was determined to give that message. He saw that nothing would change my mind; I was determined to finish what I had begun. I am thankful that I can't remember all the hardships of those days, but I do remember the day that I was assigned to give my chapel message. I was prepared!

I stood before the students and faculty and my words flowed freely. It seemed a new strength filled my body and voice. I expounded on my life verse, "I can do all things through Christ who strengthens me" (Phil. 4:13 NKJV), and also on another special verse during my crucial days, Isaiah 40:26–31. I emphasized the last verse, 31: "But they that wait upon the Lord shall renew their strength. They shall mount up with wings like eagles; they shall run and not be weary; they shall walk and not faint" (TLB). That was exactly what I had done! I had waited upon the Lord moment by moment. My strength had been renewed to do what was thought medically impossible; I had walked without fainting.

I was a living testimony to those profound scripture verses, which I had leaned on so heavily during those struggling days. Needless to say, I astounded my physician!

However, he insisted that I could not march down the aisle with my senior class to get my diploma. The Lord had taken me through everything else, and I knew, by faith, He would continue to give me strength through the commencement exercises. My mother, Mama Charles, and two of my brothers came for my graduation. I did not tell them what Dr. Culley had told me. I had on my cap and gown and marched with the others to receive my diploma. It appeared the doctor was expecting me to collapse. But I claimed God's promises as my own, and I proved Him true!

Graduation Completed, but What Next?

My return to my Mississippi home was, to me, a time to wait and see what God would do. I kept the appointment that Dr. Culley had made with a New Orleans heart specialist. After his tests and examination, he informed me that I might be able to work part time at a later time, but that I should forget about continuing any youth work. Furthermore, he recommended complete rest for one year, and then see how my heart was reacting. He discontinued the nose drops as he said they were a strong stimulant; he advised avoiding all stimulants found in medications, foods, drinks, stress, exercises, and in my entire way of life. His consultation was a beneficial education for my lifetime! He gave me a ray of hope and encouragement and commended me for my persistence.

Several months later, a minister approached me after church one Sunday and told me that a job was waiting for me in a nearby town—my reaction was amazement, but I listened, as he was adamant. Thinking I would not be accepted because I was not trained to be a high school English teacher, I applied for an interview only because I felt rested and had been doing exceptionally well. However, I informed them that I had a bachelor's degree in Christian education. Surprisingly, they were interested more than ever when they learned that, because the school board members were all church leaders in their community.

My dad drove me the forty miles for this appointment, and on our way home, he decided to return a different way. As we approached a small town, I began having chest pains. Dad found a doctor who gave me nitroglycerin tablets. When we arrived in our town, I told Dad to return to work and I'd drive home. I pulled into the driveway and fell over the steering wheel with excruciating chest pain. Family members carried me into the house and called the doctor. I wanted the job and pleaded with my doctor to help me. He said that if I avoided all stress and stimulants, and rested in a happy atmosphere for the four months before the new school year began, my positive attitude would prepare me for the job.

During those war years, the school system had instituted a special emergency certificate for people like me with a bachelor's degree in Christian education. I arrived at the school on the designated date; I accepted my assignment, and worked for three full years with no health problems.

Teaching in the South, and then returning to DC to be with my now sick dad meant facing many changes. Dad was in poor health and needed me. Again, the Lord worked out all the details. I had my civil-service status and had no problem getting a job in the *same* office where he worked in the Navy Department. Luck? No. Faith! Only faith is in my vocabulary.

My eyes had been on California for some time. When my dad's office was moved to Pennsylvania, I was praying for his health to improve so I could somehow fulfill my dream of moving to California. *It just so happened* that my high-school friend, June, who had introduced me to Fourth Church in Washington, DC, had married and moved to Pasadena, California. One day I received a letter saying that if I wanted to move to Pasadena, I had a job as church secretary at her church. She advised me to submit a resume to make it official. Then the affirmative reply came from the pastor.

I had a physical examination before leaving Pennsylvania, and the exam showed a lump in my breast. Thus, it was necessary to have surgery, which was a deciding factor as to whether or not California would be my next residence. The nurses at the hospital were aware of my eagerness to get the biopsy report. As I was wheeled back to my room following surgery, a nurse ran to my side and said, "You're on your way to California!"

A New Life in California

Recovery was fast, and my dad and I left Harrisburg, Pennsylvania, via our home in Mississippi on our way to Pasadena. In two short weeks, he returned to Harrisburg in much better health. My heart was broken to see him leave, knowing he'd be alone again. For me, it was another new city on the opposite side of the United States with many challenges facing me!

My friend, June, and her family kindly took me "under their wings" and made life very happy and comfortable in my new surroundings and church.

The church people were receptive and loving, which made my new job a joy in spite of my meager income. But one job led to another, until I began working with a Christian doctor who was deeply involved in medical research. This interesting position caused me to literally bury myself in my work.

Then Dad became very ill again and was forced to retire. Dad had Parkinson's disease and other health problems; he needed someone to care for him. I loved him and offered to be responsible for his welfare. Therefore, my brothers sent him by plane to California to live with me. The doctors where I worked at Loma Linda University, Los Angeles did an evaluation of his condition, but his Parkinson's disease was too advanced for any new medication. I was living in a duplex apartment, on the edge of Pasadena in Eagle

Rock, but my apartment was too small to care for him properly. My heart's desire was to have him comfortable in a house.

The doctor with whom I worked was moving to Turlock, California. I had other offers to work for doctors, but I knew I needed to make a change so I could spend time with Dad. To be self-employed seemed to be the only answer, but what? I applied for a position as a salesperson with the *World Book Encyclopedia,* but that meant I had a sales quota. That was a new experience and somewhat frightening! I prayed and asked my friends at my new church, the Hollywood Presbyterian Church, to pray with me. In fact, at that time, we single young adults were having Bible studies at my home. They had met my dad and saw the necessity for me to be with him. This new venture required many changes. The responsibilities were great! I knew that Dad and I had to live on my income, but I also knew that the Lord would give me wisdom and guidance in my decisions. He had never failed me in the past, and I knew He never would.

My acceptance of the new job and buying a home at the same time were overwhelming. This seemed at the time the biggest step of faith I had taken. Thank God, I had not been extravagant, but I had worked hard and saved as much as possible.

Continuing in medical research with another doctor at the Loma Linda University meant that I worked late-night hours on this second job while my dad was asleep, arriving home sometimes at two or three o'clock in the morning. My wonderful neighbors kept an eye on him.

I worked for one month as a salesperson with *World Book Encyclopedia* and saw unbelievable sales. I set my quotas and hours each day and amazingly never had to leave Dad alone for any length of time. Within one month, I was advanced to a manager, but my responsibilities increased. During this new adventure, I found a home in Pasadena, which required taking on a second mortgage. However, as I packed to move, my dad unpacked the boxes. When we moved to our new home, as I unpacked, he packed . . .

He dabbled with the thermostat, the door locks, and the stove. I never knew what to expect. But I could never scold my dad; he thought he was helping me. His delight was to make me happy. God was so good to me! Never once did I miss paying a bill—and I doubled my second mortgage payments!

Dad and I were comfortable and excited over my first home, which had a big yard for him to walk around in and enjoy the flowers. He loved the outside, but his walks sometimes extended elsewhere, so I had to call the police to search for him. His written identification in his wallet got him safely home several times by kind people and the police. I was eventually forced to stop working at night. His confusion worsened; sometimes he stood in a corner of the hall and didn't know to turn around to get where he had started. Or he tried putting his shirt on his feet, thinking it was his pants. He called me sometimes at 4 A.M. saying he was going to milk the cows or do other chores.

One morning about two o'clock, I heard him fall into the tub after he walked into the bathroom. That night I rushed him to the hospital with a heart problem. This began to be a regular occurrence. If I didn't work, I could not pay our bills. I called his retired sister and asked if she could come. When she came, he didn't know her at times, which made her angry. So both of them had to be calmed. As soon as the doctor gave permission for him to travel, his sister took him to Mississippi to my three brothers, who put him in a nursing home for constant care.

What a void I experienced without my dad! I missed him, especially every time I entered the house. It was a joy to care for him, and he appreciated everything I did. He never spoke an unkind word. But I had bought the house mainly for him and now he was gone.

One day I found a lady who had a kennel of poodles. I was so thrilled with one little brown poodle that was for sale. This was the beginning of a new life for me; another exciting story! More doors of opportunities opened in my new work, and now I had a little companion in my home. Later, I got more.

Challenges Mixed with Pain

More challenges came. I was off from work for one year with a blood clot from knee surgery, and my doctor recommended I get a

Medic Alert bracelet because of the blood-thinner drug that I was on for ten years. This drug could cause hemorrhaging after an accident, or whatever, so the bracelet could save my life. Shortly after the knee problem, I tore a muscle in the other leg, necessitating crutches and other obstacles that created hardships. It seemed I had nothing but challenges and opportunities before me. I realized that everybody has hindrances, but I resolved to do the best I could. Furthermore, the Lord always provided my needs, whatever they were.

As I advanced in my work, I had the opportunity to teach research skills in my assigned schools. The doors opened wide and sales increased. Thus, I received a trip to five European countries and also many other awards.

But, an injured spine took me off work permanently. Then as is typical to such an injury, the diagnosis of arthritis led to a prognosis that I would become increasingly more dependent on others. What a painful time in my life! But my physical condition could have been worse.

The medical advice given me was to move to Mississippi to be near my relatives so that I would not be alone. I eventually moved to Mississippi with the big challenge of building a home. Pain was constant, but my little poodles kept my attention on them and their love. One day, while I was watering my outdoor plants about 75 feet from my house, my heart started racing, and I was weak.

Why, after all those years, I thought, *did this have to happen again!* That flare-up was the warning to start living within my limitations. The added pain from severe osteoarthritis, costochronditis (inflammation relating to, or joining the rib and costal cartilage, which has symptoms of a heart attack when acute), fibromyalgia (a form of muscular rheumatism with severe pain, fatigue, and the feeling of a "persistent flu"), TMJ (arthritis in the temporomandiblar joint, symptoms of a combined ear and toothache with difficulty to open mouth), Abducens palsy (sixth cranial nerve)—then bursitis, sciatica, hypertension, a second back surgery, Meniere's disease, vestibular nerve section, cerebral aneurysm surgery, heart problem, allergies, chronic bronchitis, asthma, and now Acephalgic migraine—all made me realize that if I were to live beyond a mere existence, I had to take charge of pain. But I knew that my physical condition could be worse.

I am blessed with the abundant joy and peace that only comes from the Almighty One, who meets my every need and gives me new strength each day. How can I help but say "To God be the glory for the great things He has done" in the past, in the present, and, I know, in the future. I accept all painful situations as a *challenge*—whether caused by my body, people, weather, or whatever. Therefore, I have turned all my problems into an expectation of seeing great and mighty things because the great Jehovah God is my Shepherd. I only want my life to glorify Him—through it all.

Chapter Twelve

Arthritis: A Turning Point

One evening as I watched the TV news, a raging fire in California was consuming everything in its path. Spellbound, I watched the firefighters prepare for a backfire line. Their fierce determination was shown in their swift movements, not knowing if they were too late in their battle. The owners of the homes and the TV news crew stood by tensely, observing each unfolding moment.

Impending danger, or doom, showed clearly on anxious faces. The firefighters used shovels, picks, chain saws, and manpower to clear the ground for a firebreak. At one moment the wind seemed in their favor, then it suddenly shifted and the fire raced up the hill. Everyone went into action.

Suddenly, I pictured arthritis as that raging unpredictable fire. Arthritis flare-ups demand immediate medical attention. The "shovels, picks, chain saws, and manpower" help minimize the pain. Arthritis flare-ups put stress on the body, especially for those with multiple health problems, a condition that doctors call "comorbidity." Comorbidity is common, and more so with age. Some people have concurrent diabetes, arthritis, and other problems, which may create a potentially dangerous situation during an acute arthritis flare-up. Treatment will fluctuate as the various ailments clamor for attention.

My arthritis was "triggered" by a severe fall. It happened so fast that I don't know why I fell. I had rushed down the ramp from a meeting room into the storage/supply room, and within a split second, I was lying on the concrete floor, writhing in pain. My doctor's words rang through my mind: *You need to break a leg to slow down.*

Then I thought, *It took more than my leg—my back is broken.* Lying there, unable to move, gave me time to recall the punishment my body had endured with late hours of constant work, pushing, pushing, day after day. A demanding position had me going full speed, but I had delved into interesting jobs from the South, to the East Coast, and on to the West Coast. In reality, I was a workaholic and enjoyed every minute in my determination to be successful. Enthusiasm was bubbling over in me; in fact, the one word co-workers used to describe me was "enthusiastic."

When one of my co-workers found me on the floor, she frantically tried to help me. I screamed, "Don't touch me! I can't move; give me time. I will be all right."

She replied, "If you can't get up, I'll call an ambulance." My pleas for patience got through, however, and she waited, helpless. Finally, with effort and pain, I was gingerly moved to a couch in the meeting room.

It was Saturday; our meeting had ended. Everyone left, except Dorine, who had urgent work to finish for a special school project. I worked with her briefly, took some medication, and gave in to the pain. As soon as she left, I lay down in the meeting room, which adjoined my home.

Upon awakening with a terrible pounding headache and painful body, I knew it was imperative to see a doctor. But I determined to endure the pain until Monday when my doctor could see me. When my physician saw me early that Monday, he gave me ten cortisone injections; my hips, neck, back, right shoulder, and knees had all sustained physical damage. After his evaluation of the X-rays of my lower back, he prescribed heat treatments, pelvic traction, and medication.

With no improvement within two weeks, he referred me to an orthopedist who prescribed a lower-back support, a neck brace, and physical therapy three times a week for three months. But at the end of that time, there was no change. Therefore, my family physician referred me to another orthopedist who discontinued the traction and the back support, but continued with the neck brace. He said the traction was aggravating my back pain, and he began what he called "conservative treatments" of heat and rest.

During those months, my work was badly neglected.

We were beginning a new year. Never before had I ordered as many supplies or planned such a full year. I was going strong. But undue stress brought on hypertension. Everything was out of control—and my body knew it. My normal lifestyle had come to a sudden halt.

Surgery and More

Seventeen months later, after seeing several orthopedists, a myelogram confirmed the diagnosis of a ruptured disc in the lumbar area. Surgery and complications resulted in a twenty-one day hospitalization. My comeback was slow and discouraging. It was a very happy day when I was able to walk a short distance outdoors with my poodles. I felt optimistic and thought, *maybe my goals would be reached in the next company year.* Shortly thereafter, I awakened early one morning with a painful sensation in my hips—as if a rod had been thrust through one hip to the other. I couldn't move without using my arms to lift or turn my body.

Because my accident had been work-related, I was sent to several specialists, including a psychiatrist. Later, my company lawyer said that a psychiatrist is always included in the group of physicians for work-related cases. The psychiatrist's office visit was most interesting. When I entered his office, he directed me to sit in a certain chair on the side of the room for the consultation. He presumably continued working at his desk. Sinking into the worn, low-bottom chair put me into an extremely uncomfortable position. I was miserable and squirmed constantly. Then he began asking questions, watching me closely. Unable to concentrate on his interrogation because of the discomfort, I requested to sit else-where because of the severe pain. He directed me to a chair in front of his desk. Like a bolt of lightning, his expression and atti-tude changed. He was aware of the genuineness of my complaint, and dismissed me, saying, "You don't need to see me, you need to consult an orthopedic physician."

A wonderful consolation during those horrendous days was the love and attention of my neighbors, friends, and especially, my three little poodles. The two elderly ladies who lived next door and I would often reminisce over the memorable experiences we had shared with my poodles. When we discussed that I should write about some of their little antics, my "grandmas'" encourage-ment was immediate, and proved continuous and persuasive. Thus, I began writing my first nonfiction book.

It took several years of recalling some of the exciting events with my "little girls," and it helped to turn my thoughts away from my aches and pain. When unable to sleep at night, I focused my thoughts on some of the unforgettable happenings with my poodles and jotted down those reflections. Little by little, the stories were written, and finally my book was published. My poodles and our grandmas were the best therapy during those trying days of endur-ing the hardships of no job, no medical relief, no bright hope for my future, and waiting on God to direct my day-by-day pace. I clung to the promise that God gave Moses in Deuteronomy 31:6: "Be strong and of a good courage, fear not, nor be afraid of them: for the Lord thy God, he it is that doth go with thee; he will not fail thee, nor forsake thee" (KJV).

The Word of God strengthened and helped me face each prob-lem with courage, believing that God would also go with me and neither fail nor forsake me at any time. To whom else could I turn? When down, we often learn that *only* God is still beside us, help-ing, comforting, guiding, and providing every need.

A period of three years had elapsed since my back surgery. Time, pain, and unpleasant medical consultations had added emotional and mental trauma to my physical suffering. I turned the wheels and ventured into another community, to a private orthopedic specialist. He had no connection with any insurance or government agency and was interested only in my welfare. Although the initial accident report filed six years earlier substantiated injuries to my neck, right shoulder, back, hips, and both lower extremities, this orthopedist discussed with me his findings in a way I'd not heard before. Upon completion of his thorough examination and X-ray analysis, he had concrete evidence of a diagnosis that, he said, needed immediate medical attention. He gave a discouraging prognosis. His report read, in part: "Gradual worsening of her polyarthritis—osteoarthritic cervical, dorsal, and lumbosacral spine—regardless of therapy. . . . Probably increasing pain and gradual increase in disability."

After thoroughly discussing with me my various problems, my orthopedist told me he had consulted with my personal physician about his findings and neither of them felt I should continue living alone, and they advised a move to Mississippi to be near my family. His words literally shattered my dreams. I had a comfortable home in Southern California, and so many friends. Moving from there to Mississippi would be such a drastic change. Although it was evident that I could not work, it was difficult to accept that fact. At every office visit, he asked if I had made plans to move. His pessimistic picture made me realize that steps had to be taken *by me*, for a change. Those were dark, dreary, discouraging days. It was exceedingly helpful to have a family physician who also cared and did everything to make life as bearable as possible.

Arthritis also caused fatigue, which was another distress that was hard to accept. Additional pounds, put on by cortisone, created an extra burden for my joints.

On one visit, an orthopedic physician asked me to pick up a piece of equipment that was sitting on a table. I was amazed at his request but attempted to lift the device. When I exclaimed that it was too heavy and the weight hurt my back, he used it as an object lesson. "That only weighs twenty pounds, and you are twenty pounds overweight," he said. After losing thirteen pounds, I did have some relief. My diet and persistency, combined with balancing rest and exercise, made me realize that an active role in my treatment was vital. It was a trial-and-error process, one that would become a lifetime procedure.

I also enrolled in an aquatic class for arthritis. What a joy it was to move about in that warm water in a way I had not been able to do! Relief, though, was temporary. My schedule was great, and I wondered what would happen if I did move to Mississippi. The thought of not being able to continue such a therapy program delayed a decision.

It took months for me to realize the need to sell my home and accept a new way of life. My happy days were forever recorded in my memories. Some nights, unable to sleep, I wandered slowly throughout the house, scanning the details of each room. Then, I lay in bed with closed eyes, visualizing the entire house. Some hours were spent taking pictures of different views of the inside and outside of my home; I was determined that nothing would be erased from my mind. The choice would be the California desert or Mississippi, to be near my family. Visiting the desert, with its agreeable climate, wonderful spas, and fresh air, appealed to my strong desire to move there. However, a friend and her son said they would drive with me to Mississippi to see if God might have a place for me there. I only wanted to be where the Lord wanted me to be.

Property Purchased in Mississippi

Within two days of our scheduled departure from the visit to Mississippi, I found a beautiful location on which to build. With time running out, immediate steps were taken to buy the property. House plans were selected, an architect was hired, and I returned to California with the big job of deciding on a house plan—and selling my California home.

What a turning point that fall had been for me! One day, all was going so beautifully, then suddenly, everything was changed. It meant a complete turnabout. Seven months were spent in the routine of slowly packing and preparing for the final move, while also in the process of selling my home. In the meantime, I had to cope with the arthritic pain. Some days were worse than others, and the packing drudgery called for days of rest and therapy as the activity was too much for my body.

My doctor refused to give me more cortisone and ordered a TENS (Transcutaneous Electrical Nerve Stimulation) unit on a trial basis. Time was all that was needed to get adjusted, and I have been grateful to this day for his prescribing the TENS. It has been helpful, especially for my sciatica and lower back.

Besides packing, there was so much business to handle. Dealing with real estate calls and visits, making preparations for a long-distance move, and a sudden change in my lifestyle—all aggravated my body aches. Nevertheless, the huge job during those days required much wisdom and strength, but everything had to be done according to the schedule dictated by my arthritis.

A dear cousin from New Orleans came several weeks early to help in my last weeks of moving. We shared a love for my poodles, and she was considerate of my inability to be active and go places as we had on her previous visits. It wasn't long before she, too, had trouble walking. She didn't want to complain, because she was afraid I would insist she see my doctor. But the time came when it was expedient that she have a medical consultation. After an examination and tests, surgery was scheduled. My heart was crushed when I learned that it was too late, because cancer was rampant in her body. The prognosis was that she had only a few months to live. Immediately, I took my home off the market and made plans for taking care of her in my home as long as necessary. When her young son came from New Orleans, he was in shock and dismay to see his suffering mother.

The day we took Lucille from the hospital to my home, a real estate agent called to say he had a client who insisted on seeing my home. When he was reminded that my home was off the market temporarily because of an emergency, he insisted. His clients from San Diego wanted to look inside before leaving the Pasadena area. After explaining the situation, he pleaded for only a few minutes for his clients, who would understand the disarray, and it would not affect what they wanted to see. Reluctantly, I consented, and within a day, they accepted my asking price. The Lord was in control and made me realize that He would work out every detail—and He did!

When Lucille was able to travel home to New Orleans, I saw her alive once more. This was another turning point in my life; she would have made such a difference in my life in my Mississippi residence. She was like a sister to me, and I loved her dearly.

A week before the moving date, my oldest brother came to drive my four poodles and me, with my trailer, to Mississippi. During the short time my brother was in my home, he saw one miracle after another. He observed transactions that would ordinarily take days or weeks, consummated in the wink of an eye. He is a businessman and was astounded. Charles turned to me one day and said, "Sis, I know the Lord is with you. I am seeing miracles happen in front of my eyes. It is incredible to see how smoothly and orderly all these things are finalizing so quickly." The Lord was with us as we traveled to Mississippi and continued to work one miracle after another as the house took shape, and my poodles and I moved into our new home.

Arthritis continued to be a tremendous handicap as adjustments were made to my new surroundings and climate. However, a friend who also has arthritis and many other problems, recommended her physician to me. That was one of the best steps I took in getting as much help as possible for my many health problems. This physician encouraged me physically, emotionally, and mentally, although I don't believe he ever realized the self-reliance he instilled in me through his treatments, consultations, and encouragement. His advice to attend an arthritis support group and an arthritis aquatic class, and his referrals to other physicians, always resulted in a beneficial discussion and evaluation. My confidence in his medical knowledge and judgment gave me a realistic outlook on living with arthritis and coping with pain.

Statistics in a letter and booklet sent to me by Gregory W. Heath, D.Sc., M.P.H., Epidemiologist, Statistics and Epidemiology Branch of the Centers for Disease Control and Prevention, showed "Arthritis—the leading cause of disability." In their *Morbidity and Mortality Weekly Report*, October 14, 1994, a survey reported that "nine in 100 adults said they have trouble climbing a flight of stairs or walking a quarter-mile . . . joint ailments are the nation's leading disability." Dr. Heath noted that "these reports are based on nationally representative samples of non-institutionalized persons living in the United States." An article said, the "survey was conducted in household interviews with 97,133 people between October 1991 and January 1992. About 196 million people fall into the surveyed age group. . . ." Arthritis is certainly not easy to live with, and it does not promise a bright future as far as pain is concerned.

Coping with a moment-by-moment arthritic body, I have learned to trust and obey the One who created me and knows all about my body. I am determined to take advantage of everything I physically can, to do whatever is medically prescribed, and not to give into a debilitating disease by being inactive, as long as I have the strength to fight. I will also keep a positive attitude and anchor my hope and faith in my ever-present God. Only God knows the trauma associated with enduring pain, both physical and emotional. It has turned my world upside down. But I know that my life is in His hands, and arthritis—a turning point that happened years ago—has made my faith, courage, and hope anchored deeper in my Lord.

Jesus is Lord of my life, so I just walk hand in hand with Him at all times. There is no turning back, because He has proved Himself my constant Companion and Comforter.

In spite of pain, life is sweeter and happier because of the assurance I have that the Lord is in control of my life. Someday I will be free of this feeble body and will have *no pain* . . .

Until that day, I rest in Him, knowing that my life verse, Philippians 4:13 remains true: "I can do everything through him who gives me strength" (NIV). I know that I will always have that strength because "they that wait upon the Lord, shall renew their strength. They shall mount up with wings like eagles" (Isa. 40:31 TLB). I do wait on the Lord; I am strengthened day by day, and, therefore, I can soar like the eagle above all fleeting painful clouds!

"Mount up with wings like eagles, and He'll renew your strength."
—from a song by Alma Welch

Chapter Thirteen

A Screaming Body, but a Joyful Heart

A joyful heart is good medicine, But a broken spirit dries up the bones. (Prov. 17:22 NASB)

This proverb has been on my mind since the moment I started writing on the subject of pain. If one has a body that is in so much pain that it is silently, or verbally, screaming, how can there be joy? Regardless of all the medications prescribed, only a joyful heart can help the drugs work.

How can a person with cerebral palsy have a joyful heart? As a youngster, David Ring begged to die because he had cerebral palsy, which was caused by damage at birth. In some cases, the damage may happen before, or even after birth. If you have never heard Rev. David Ring preach, read the testimony below, which he gave permission to be printed in this book. You will have a different opinion about a person with cerebral palsy after reading his message.

Two horrifying accidents and a young lady's life of temporary blindness are also related here for publication. I don't believe that mere words can truly epitomize what I am saying, but four individuals who have, or have had, "a screaming body," have expressed their personal experiences and then declared their joyful hearts in spite of their suffering.

An Unlikely Preacher

As I watched TV one Sunday morning, a distinguished looking, brown-haired young man stood behind a pulpit. His face shone with a joy that is seen on few faces today, but as soon as he spoke—in one of the sweetest voices I have ever heard—I knew that this outstanding, brave young man had cerebral palsy.

With his permission, I am sharing most of his message in his own words:

> Some of you have looked me over, up one side, and down the other. That is OK; I am looking you over, too. I was born with cerebral palsy; therefore, I talk a little bit differently, but I promise you that you can not catch it. You have to be born with it. You say you can not understand me. I don't want that to bother you. My talking is like an old wart; I get to grow on you.
>
> If there is a passage in the Bible that sums up what I want to say to you, it's 2 Corinthians 12:9–10, which is my message: "And he said unto me, My grace is sufficient for thee: for my strength is perfect in weakness. Most gladly therefore will I rather glory in my infirmities (circumstances, situations), that the power of Christ may rest upon me. Therefore, I take pleasure in infirmities (in the way I am) . . . for when I am weak, then I am strong" (KJV). My message to you today is God's grace is sufficient for me and you.
>
> *Why* do bad things happen to God's people? My life began in 1953 in Jonesboro, Arkansas, with cerebral palsy. The oxygen couldn't get to my brain; therefore I was born dead for eighteen minutes. I walk with a limp and I talk funny; I was born with cerebral palsy. *Why* do bad things happen to God's people? My dad was a Baptist preacher; I am a preacher's kid. I went to church so much that I went to church nine months before I was ever born. When you are a preacher's kid, you go to church all your life, whether you like it or not; you have no option.

I thank God for giving me a momma and dad who took me to church; they didn't send me. When I was eleven years old, my dad got sick. In November 1968, my dad went to be with the Lord because of cancer of the liver. I know my dad is in heaven today having a good time with Jesus—because the Bible says "to be absent from the body, and to be present with the Lord" (2 Cor. 5:8b KJV).

Why do bad things happen to God's people? I am the baby of eight children—a spoiled brat—and my momma gave me everything I wanted and sometimes things I didn't want. I am a number-one momma's-boy; you can tell by looking at me because I've got that momma's baby face. I loved my momma, and my momma loved me. Every morning we loved each other (with a hug), and we told each other that we loved each other. I loved my momma. Everybody needs momma-love—and momma-touch. When I was fourteen, Momma became sick and she had an operation on her neck. Two months later, in July 1968, the doctor told us that Momma had cancer, and she had six months to live. *Why* do bad things happen to God's people? I got down on my knees every day crying, "God, please don't take my momma—God, please don't take my momma—God, please don't take my momma. She's *all* I have."

In October 1968, God took my momma. I saw her go from 185 pounds to 57 pounds; it tore me up. I didn't want to live. I wanted to die. My family gave me everything they could, but my family couldn't give me the love or the touch that only Momma could give me, or the joy that only Momma could give me.

Everywhere I went, somebody pointed a finger and said, "That boy walks funny; that boy talks funny; oh, look, that boy can't do nothing right." It's no fun to be made fun of. I couldn't go home to Momma and say, "Momma, somebody made fun of me today." She couldn't put her arms around me and make it all right.

I laid in bed every night with tears, begging to die. I was longing to be in my momma's arms one more time. If I could be in my momma's arms one more time, the pain would go away. I was lonely! I told my family to give up on me. I'm a no-good cripple; I'll never do anything; I'll never be anything. Everybody but one sister gave up on me. She encouraged me. She wanted me to go to school. But I didn't want to be the laughingstock of the student body. It's no fun walking down the hallway and have some one laugh at me because my body is a little bit different. She wanted me to go to church; I didn't want to go to church. I'd been to church all my life. I'm the preacher's kid; I know the lingo. We all learned John 3:16—but if God loves me *why, why* did God take my father? If God loves me, *why* did God take my momma?

And if God loves me, *why* did He give me a crippled body? If God loves me, *why* did God pick on me? If God loves me, *why* is God angry with me? If God loves me, *why* do bad things happen to God's people? If God loves me, *why* is God breaking my heart?

Why do bad things happen to God's people? I'm sure that many, most, if not all of you, ask that same question—*Why? Why? Why?* If God loves me, *why?* My sister wanted me to go to church, but I didn't want to go. One night I went to church to get my sister off my back. That night I sat down and when the preacher got up to preach, I said, "Man, I wish you would shut up."

He shut up, but the Lord Jesus spoke up. The Lord came to me, knocked on my heart, and said, "David, if you will only listen to me; I am standing at your heart and knocking. If you will open your heart, I will come in and I will have fellowship with you forever and forever." No one ever told me about that relationship with Jesus. No one ever told about that relationship with the King of Kings, the Lord of Lords. No one ever told me a lot of things. No one ever told me how the Lord could change a life. I said on my knees, "Jesus, if you are really up there, if you really love me, if you really love me and will come into my life, then come into my life. I'm a lonely crippled boy. I'm a nobody. I want to be a somebody!"

On April 17, 1970, I became a somebody—a brand new creature. I'm not lonely anymore. I'm happy. I've been to the doctor—Dr. Jesus—and I didn't have to be in the office two hours. Jesus gave me a new thing: He took away my loneliness and gave me happiness. I'm not lonely anymore because I've been to Jesus, who took my sorrow and gave me joy—joy that is unspeakable and full of glory. Look at me, folks. Look at me, people! I still walk with a limp. I still talk funny, but, oh, the joy that floods my soul because Jesus "touched me and made me whole." I thank God for giving me the privilege to be born with cerebral palsy. *Why?* So that God's glory can be shown in my life. All my life I've been saying, "Why, why, why?" I've been told I'm a cripple; I'm a cripple; I'm a cripple. All my life I'm been discouraged, but, thank God, the Bible says, "we are (I'm) more than conquerors"! (Rom. 8:37*b* KJV).

They told me that I'm a nobody but the Bible says I'm a somebody: I'm a child of the King. They told me that I can't do nothing, but the Bible says "with God all things are possible" (Mark 10:27 NKJV). They told me I would never be a preacher, but I am. In 1971, God called me to preach. I was lying in bed, minding my own business, and God said, "David, I want you to preach." I said, "Who, me? Lord, I can't speak. Are you sure you want me to preach, Lord? I talk funny. People can't understand me. Lord, I have cerebral palsy. Take a second look at me, Lord, and then call me."

And He still called me to preach. I got out of my bed and got my Bible and turned to Philippians 4:13 which says, "I can do all things through Christ who strengthens me" (NKJV). I'm not going to let cerebral palsy slow me down. I have cerebral palsy. What's your problem? *I have cerebral palsy. What's your problem?*

Why are you crying the blues? Why are you down in the dumps? Why are you down in the mouth? God gave you a healthy body. What are you doing with it for the Kingdom of God? Don't whine—but shine! Shine for the glory of God. They told me I'd never make it in evangelism. They told me that I'd never make it. They told me that nobody would invite me to speak in their church. Well, I have spoken *only* 263 times in the last twelve months. When I get a little bit more invitations, I will go full time . . . God doesn't want my ability. God wants my availability! I can't even say Jesus plainly.

What's your problem, healthy man? What's your problem, healthy woman? What's your problem, healthy teenager? What are you doing for the glory of God? I have cerebral palsy; what's your problem? My own family—my own family—discouraged me. They told me, "David, you won't find a wife."

"Why not?"

"You're a cripple. No woman would want to live with a cripple, a handicapped man, so don't even look for a wife. You are not good enough."

But in 1981, God and me showed them a thing or two. I found me a dynamite wife, one of God's precious gifts. She has prayed for me and stood with me through thick and thin. I thank God for my little wife, Karen. They told me that I would never be a daddy. But I am—not once, not twice, but three times, and number four is on the way. Pretty good, huh? Every time I look at my children, April, Ashely, Nathan and (now) Amy Joy, all I can say is "to God be the glory for the great things He has done."

I know where I've been: I'm the little crippled boy that lay in bed every night crying my eyes out. I'm the little crippled boy that they made fun of. I'm the little crippled boy that don't have no momma or daddy. I'm the little crippled boy begging to die. Don't feel sorry for me. When I get to heaven, I'll have a brand new body. I won't walk with a limp anymore. I'm not going to talk funny anymore. I'm going to walk and talk like Jesus. I know where I've been, but, praise God, I know where I am. I know what I am today. All that I am is only by the grace of God. And I know where I'm going.

One day I'll see my momma and daddy. I miss my momma and daddy. I would love to go home and see my momma. I would love to call my momma and say, "I love you." I would love to go home at Christmastime and find a present under the tree and open that gift and see the card with those two words, "Love, Momma." I would love to go home and get a birthday card once each year and see two dynamite words, "Love, Momma."

We don't appreciate the words until they stop coming. I would love to have my daddy hear me preach, and after I preached, let my daddy tell me everything I did wrong. I would love that. But I can't ever have that. There is a song I'd like to sing after my life story that sums up what I've tried to share with you. God didn't call me to sing; God called me to preach. I love to sing this song. I don't sing from my lips; I sing from my heart.

Now, piano player, make me look good. You say what key do you want it in? I don't care what you pick. By the time we get finished, I'll be all over the keyboard. Let this song bless you. You are looking at a thirty-five-year-old man who has victory in Jesus.
—*Rev. David Ring, Orlando, Florida*

What a blessing! A powerful message from the lips and heart of the Rev. David Ring ended with a soul-stirring song. As he sang, "Victory in Jesus," his countenance radiated with the joy of Jesus. The TV cameras scanned the audience, showing tears streaming down faces of all ages. Hearts were broken and humbled as the words flowed from the depth of Reverend Ring's soul.

Only God knows the many lives that have been changed by the testimony of this "little crippled boy." To hear him say "I have cerebral palsy; what's your problem?" are piercing words that will always ring in my ears, and, I believe, in the ears and hearts of many people.

A handsome young man who had begged to die because of a screaming, crippled body, proclaimed to the world that day, and he continues to proclaim, that only the Lord Jesus can change a broken spirit into a heart filled with joy.

A Young Girl's Severe Burn

While Rev. David Ring lives with a chronic condition, a dear friend, Linda Williams, endured a painful accident in her home, which affected her way of life temporarily.

We are unaware of the occurrence of severe injuries in the home, as mentioned in chapter 1, but statistics are startling. I deciphered more facts from one of the tables in the *Accident Facts 1994 Edition of the National Safety Council*: Severe injuries in the home occur every five seconds and a death every twenty-three minutes; and the number per day were 18,100 severe injuries and sixty-two deaths.

Linda has written about her horrendous experience and the comfort that only the Lord God can give during such a stressful time from a very serious burn with horrible complications. The following is her story, which is told exclusively for this book:

> During my third year as a student at the University of California at Riverside, I lived in a condominium, renting a room from the owner. The college was on winter break, and I had plans to spend the holidays with my family in Pasadena. But I had to work until a few days before Christmas, so I was still staying in the condo.
>
> On December 22, 1987, I returned from work, and began preparing my meal of hamburgers and fries. I put the patties in the oven first and began working with the potatoes for fries. I put a pot of oil on the stove, then sliced the potatoes. The bowl

of french fries was in my left hand as I opened the vent with my right hand. When I opened the vent, the screen fell off and hit the pot handle. The pot flipped up and the oil went flying . . . I don't remember if I was in pain at that time. But I do remember the look on my sister's face (she was staying with me), just after it happened. It scared me. I vaguely remember screaming.

Erin, who lived in the condo across the courtyard, heard a scream and rushed to see what was wrong. I still don't remember any pain. It was almost Christmas, so the condo owner and her renters had already left to spend the holidays with family. But God made sure that I was not there alone. Also, because it was so close to Christmas, Erin's brother was home for the holidays; he was a medic in the Marines! I think he's the one who called the ambulance that took me to the burn unit in San Bernardino. I had the nicest, most patient nurses there who answered my many questions.

When I first got to the burn unit, my burn, diagnosed as third degree, extended from under my right arm to my hip. It was completely smooth and white. The nurse told me that this was because several layers of skin were gone. Several days after I got to the hospital, I started seeing little bumps and feeling more and more pain. I learned that the pain came as the nerve endings, which had been badly damaged, began rejuvenating themselves.

Then, added to this, just about the time the nerves began coming back, my body started showing signs of allergies to the sulfa drugs that were used to wrap the burns. They changed the dressing immediately, because someone in the burn unit had just died from a bad reaction to sulfa drugs. The alternative dressing was not as easy to get used to, because it stung into the wounds, as opposed to the cooling sensation of the sulfa drugs.

Morphine was given for the severe pain and the morphine injections were increased to help decrease the pain. I had morphine because they determined that I was probably allergic to Demerol. However, the morphine injections were quite painful! Years later, I still have two or three sites that I call "morphine wounds," where the morphine burned my skin. The morphine injections stung as the medication went into my body; but it really didn't stop the pain! It did make my body dull and listless, so I could eventually fall asleep.

I was shocked when the nurse said that each injection could sell for about $100 "on the street." Why would anybody willingly and unnecessarily submit themselves to morphine? It is not a comfortable feeling in any respect! The treatments! The nurse made an analogy as to getting a cavity filled. The dentist must first dig out the rotten "stuff" and then fill the resulting space. For a third-degree burn, the rotten skin (called "asker") must be removed before the skin graft. The process of removing the asker was extremely painful!

By this time, my nerve endings had started coming back. My body was screaming! Before I got my whirlpool treatment, I was given a shot of morphine, then the asker was pulled off with a tool that resembled tweezers. The process is every bit as painful as it sounds! I was told that this was the least painful way, but the nurse let me try an approach that I thought would be less painful. It wasn't!

After the removal of the asker, I sat in a warm, sudsy whirlpool for about twenty minutes; then came the rewrapping with yellow medication that stung. I learned that firemen get part of their training in the burn units. They learn by examining the burn and giving shots, etc. Because of the location of my burn, they were not permitted to help remove the asker from my body.

Once, during a moment of frustration, I began feeling sorry for myself and began crying. When I did, the pain actually became worse! So I started watching silly sitcoms. It is so true that "laughter does good like medicine."

Proverbs 17:22a says, "A merry heart does good, like medicine" (NKJV). I'm not sure if the pain really decreased, but it was more tolerable when I was cheerful and laughing. Because the burn began under my arm, I had to regain my range of motion. It hurt! A very pleasant physical therapist with a Jamaican accent worked diligently with me. Every morning after the TV show *I Love Lucy* went off, I knew it was time for therapy. The usual procedure was turning a crank, which was in the hall. The gadget was designed so that I would move my arm as high as I could and then back down. I tried so hard, often standing on my tiptoes to get to the top of the crank. I was not successful, but what an experience!

Another therapy was sleeping with my arm over my head. It was horrible to wake up and not be able to move my arm without a lot of pain! That, too, was a nightmare!

After the skin graft was completed, they let me go home after only sixteen days in the hospital. The "donor site" from which they took the skin was my upper thigh. This was so that the entire wound would be in the same general area. The following Monday, I had the staples removed. They attached the new skin over the burned parts! They looked like the staples used in a staple gun. I stopped counting after the removal of 120 staples. Because of the incredible pain in my right leg, I forgot about the staples. I thought I just had a cramp from being in the hospital bed so long. I did not dare tell the nurse. My mom, however, did dare. As soon as Mom told the nurse about my leg pain, he said that some people develop blood clots after having a skin graft. Upon finishing removal of the staples, he immediately took me into another room and hooked me up to a machine.

Lo and behold he was right. I had a blood clot in my right leg. Back to the hospital, but this time I went to Kaiser in Los Angeles, where my doctor had called in the results of his tests. This time the most painful endurance was the IV. Apparently, I have small veins, so they had to change the location of the IV every two or three days, because the vein would collapse.

After eleven days in Kaiser, I was back in my college classes, having missed a couple of weeks because of the holidays. I only had to withdraw from one class because I had missed too much. But in the others, I had enough time to catch up.

Just over a month after this blood clot started, my doctor signed for me to go back to work. I worked at a hospital, and one of the nurses noticed that I did everything with my right arm seemingly "fused" to my body. (I had learned to ignore the pain.) At her suggestion, I called Kaiser and I was referred to a plastic surgeon who explained the steroid treatments I needed for pain. I left his office in Los Angeles in tears after the treatment! I cried almost the entire ninety-minute drive back to Riverside. I thought I had experienced a lot of pain before, but this was a new level of pain! For three days, the pain grew worse!

When I called the doctor's office, his nurse explained some things to me. Then I realized I would just have to wait it out.

Her words appeased me, but the doctor called me later and discussed the procedure with me for about twenty minutes. As I was told, the pain gradually decreased after the first three days. Since that initial treatment, I only had one more "torture treatment" of steroids. I learned that steroid use is monitored by the government, and I had already reached the legal limit for one dosage. Even though some of the burn remained untreated, the doctor was legally unable to inject any more for about thirty days. I honestly did not think I could endure that kind of pain again, but I could really tell a big difference in the part that was treated. Therefore, I did go for another "torture treatment." They used a general anesthesia that time, but I awakened in a lot of pain. Thank God, those days are over!

The burn was mostly first degree on my face. The skin looks close to normal now years later, except that my lips and other areas have a few splotches. The other burned parts of my body are all hidden and can only be observed if I wear shorts or a tank top. I do have full range of arm motion now, also, since I personally began stretching my arm on the job without a therapist. And my praying—while stretching and groaning—*worked!* God is so good!

I never did blame God for "doing this." I thought I had done something wrong to receive all this suffering. Now I know that Satan, the destroyer, does things to try to harm us. I have learned to use the authority over that devil that God gave us in Ephesians 6:10–12: "Finally, be strong in the Lord and in his mighty power. Put on the full armor of God so that you can take your stand against the devil's schemes. For our struggle is not against flesh and blood, but against the rulers, against the authorities, against the powers of this dark world and against the spiritual forces of evil in the heavenly realms" (NIV).

Throughout that ordeal, I had incredible support from my parents. The first hospital I was in, in San Bernardino, was about three hours roundtrip east from Pasadena. They visited me every evening! The second hospital (for the blood clot) was about forty-five minutes west of Pasadena, yet they came every night to see me. Everyone from my school and church kept in touch with me.

I give God all the credit for the good things that happened. Even in difficult situations, my Lord takes such good care of me—and He does for all who believe and trust in Him, the All-Powerful One!

—*Elinda Williams, Sacramento, California*

What a joy to see the way Linda has reacted to her "screaming body" from this accident. I remember Linda growing up next door in Pasadena as an unusually gifted teenager. Between her high school and college years, she became a certified animal-health technician. Because she has always loved helping people, she also became a certified nurse's assistant. At the University of California in Riverside, she received her bachelor's degree in psychology. Her last position, as of this writing, is as a computer programmer for the state of California in Sacramento.

Her encouraging, Christian family helped in her many endeavors, but she has always been a persistent, conscientious worker. At age twenty-seven, she is a very excited and thankful young woman of many accomplishments. Within six months, on her own she bought a new car and a condominium. She is active at the Calvary Christian Center in Sacramento, sings in the choir, and is a member of the media communication ministry. Nothing can hold Linda down! She has learned to put her priorities in order: She puts God first in her life and leans on Him for His direction in everything she does. Linda claims Psalm 3:3 as a special verse: "But You, O Lord, are a shield for me, My glory and the One who lifts up my head" (NKJV).

Joey's Miracle

My attention has also been focused on another person who endured severe suffering at an early age. One of the sweetest, most outstanding, most handsome young teenagers I have had the privilege to know is Joey Bernard. At age seventeen, weighing 170 pounds and standing six feet tall, he lived to tell about an incredible accident with an 850-pound four-wheeler on top of him in a foot of water.

The following is his account of this accident and what the doctors told him they did during surgery:

My friends and I were coming out of the woods after riding for several hours in a very woody area several miles from our community. We were crossing a creek and tried to get out by climbing a big hill. Suddenly, the front end of my four-wheeler went straight up; immediately, I pushed my girlfriend off the seat, but I fell backwards with the four-wheeler landing on top of me in the creek. Six of my friends stood frozen, looking at the four-wheeler on top of me, with my head held down in one foot of water.

Impulsively, one young man jumped into the creek. With that super strength that comes only in times of emergencies, he pushed the four-wheeler off my body. With God's help, I crawled out of the water but realized I could feel nothing in my legs. They were numb! One of my friends had a motorcycle and raced off for help. The others lifted me and gently put me on the four-wheeler, behind my girlfriend. She drove out of the area very slowly. When she hit a bump, I screamed! The severity of the pain probably had me near fainting, when one of my friends caught me as I began falling off the machine.

Paramedics and the fire crew arrived. They stretched me out on the ground and stayed with me until two more paramedics arrived on four-wheelers, along with a crew from the fire department. After cutting down trees, the other paramedics arrived in a four-wheel-drive truck, gave me a pain injection, and put me on a backboard. They drove me about three miles to the waiting ambulance. My pain was just unbearable! After all the moving of my body, the first pain injection had no effect on my horrible pain. At the hospital, they gave me a lot of pain injections before they could move me for X-rays. By that time, I could only move one arm. It was then they thought I was paralyzed!

The X-rays showed my back was broken in three places; my spinal cord was knocked out of the spinal canal; I had three crushed discs in my lower back, and three more discs cracked elsewhere; I had three crushed vertebrae; and the nerve that goes from my brain to my toes was frayed in three places. Then, because of the pressure to the inside of my body by the impact of the heavy four-wheeler, my throat was ripped up to my lips. After the report, they rushed me to Providence Hospital in Mobile for more extensive medical help. It was there I was told I would need surgery as soon as the swelling went down. Those were unforgettable, painful hours waiting for surgery.

After five hours and four minutes in surgery, my doctor told me that "it was a perfect surgery." They took a bone out of my hip and fused it onto the three crushed vertebrae. They told me they repaired my three crushed discs. For the rest of my life, I am now able to walk with two 14½-inch steel rods on both sides of my spine, held by eight 4-inch screws. After being in the hospital for thirteen days, I recuperated for six weeks before slowly returning to school for about one hour a day for a few days. Then I was able to stay in school for three hours a day for the rest of the school year.

As I write this unforgettable experience about seven months later, I feel that I am almost back to my usual life. The worst position for me is sitting, but about three months after surgery, I worked at the Dairy Queen for about three hours at a time. Then only six months after surgery, I began working as a cashier at Walmart, standing about eight hours with a break about every two to three hours.

God is on my side, and I know that He worked a miracle in my life! I am doing so well that my doctor says that I can do whatever I want to do—walking, swimming, riding, or whatever—as long as I don't feel pain. People just don't know what we take advantage of every day, such as getting out of bed, sitting at the dinner table, driving a car, or even walking *without* a painful body. We don't realize we should be thankful so much for just the everyday things. Little did I realize the suffering I would endure when this picture was taken a few weeks before my accident.

All the time I went through my suffering, a Scripture verse stayed in my thoughts when I hurt too much to talk. It helped me get through many painful

Joey Bernard

days. I learned this verse at my church in our Sunday School Bible class, Proverbs 3:5*b*–6: ". . . trust the Lord completely; don't ever trust yourself. In everything you do, put God first, and he will direct you and crown your efforts with success" (TLB). My life should be a living example of what God can do if I will just trust Him. I know that I am a walking miracle! And I thank God every day that I can walk!

—*Joey Bernard, Thomasville, Alabama*

In the "Facts at a Glance" statistics given by the National Spinal Cord Injury Statistical Center, Birmingham, Alabama, vehicular accidents ranked as the *leading* cause of spinal cord injuries. Joey's accident falls in this category. But for the grace of God, he would be paralyzed today.

Facing a Life in Darkness

Another person who has endured physical and emotional suffering is a young woman, who at the early age of twenty-nine, was diagnosed with keratoconus, a rare form of blindness. She wrote, "Imagine looking at a foggy bathroom mirror; then you know what it was like for me with my blindness. My lifestyle changed; and if I could not have a successful cornea transplant, I would have to go to the rehabilitation services for the blind and learn Braille. I prayed for a donor!"

However, within ten years, she had two cornea transplants and "can now see wonderfully." It took two years of waiting for a cornea donor for her right eye and eighteen months for her left eye. During those traumatic years, she was the sole support of her child and had exorbitant medical bills. Throughout those years, she said she heard "the thunder," relating to God's voice, as she humbled herself before Him. A special Bible verse that helped get her through those horrendous days was Psalm 23:4 "Even though I walk through the valley of the shadow of death, I will fear no evil, for you are with me; your rod and your staff, they comfort me" (NIV).

This lady, Mary Lee Long-Bowen of Meridian, Mississippi, speaks before groups encouraging them to be organ donors. She reminds people to think of a "dying child (or anyone) looking up from their hospital bed, relying on God," and "maybe *you* could save a life by being a donor." She says that there are "more children under the age of ten who need a kidney, liver, or a bone marrow transplant" than there are adults who are waiting on a donor list.

The United Network for Organ Sharing (UNOS) informed me that two steps should be taken to be a donor. First, inform your entire family of your wishes; second, fill in your driver's license space stating your wishes (or in some states there may be a separate card to go with your driver's license). (See this book's appendix for UNOS's address and telephone.)

Regardless of the suffering surrounding our lives, we know that we are living "in the shadow of the Almighty," shielded "under His wings" (Ps. 91:1,4 NIV) and are protected by His angels wherever we go. The majestic, soaring eagle is a beautiful symbol of God lifting us up above the clouds of impatience, depression, and despair. Those of us who have a "screaming body" soar serenely, knowing that we have fullness of joy only in the presence of the Lord. David said in Psalm 16:11*b*: "In Thy presence is fulness of joy. . . ." (NASB).

And this ingrained reality permeates our lives with the inner peace and joy that transcends all pain! So we soar higher and higher, keeping our eyes and hearts fixed joyfully on the Almighty!

Chapter Fourteen
Taking Control

Doesn't he realize that I am in too much pain to write a book?" How could my local doctor suggest that I write a book on how I have managed my life with acute and chronic pain when he knew my suffering? His words resonated in my mind as he continually encouraged me at each office visit. *I hurt. I hurt all the time.* But if he thinks I can do it, I will.

I began an extensive study of pain, mainly arthritis pain, at the beginning of my research. The deeper I looked, the more facets of the subject I discovered.

Several years later at the Mayo Clinic, the cardiologist assigned to me said that I could serve as a good example for other patients in the management of pain. When I told him that my local physician had suggested I write a book about that subject, he encouraged me. When I scanned through the material I had accumulated, I realized that merely reading about pain from the perspective of a variety of health problems was some of the best therapy I had had. And maybe somehow, sharing both painful experiences and the coping sequence, might be of help to other sufferers. This was a great challenge.

Three Major Surgeries within Two Years

While I considered writing a book, I had three major surgeries within a two year period. The first surgery was the result of Meniere's disease. The cause of this disease is unknown, but this traumatic experience was unlike any other, with no helpful treatment available for me. Eight months before surgery, acute attacks of Meniere's disease, lasting four to ten hours, became very frequent. The advanced stage of this disease ended in my being completely debilitated, or as my surgeon stated, it left me "completely disabled."

Attacks hit with no warning, and as the disease progressed, the severity of the pressure on the upper right side of my head became agonizing. It could not be controlled, even with medications as strong as morphine.

I could not see, not even a doctor leaning over my face, during those attacks. The spinning, whirling sensation can be compared to no other spell of vertigo. The experience was torturous, horrifying helplessness. A world-renowned neurotologist in Nashville said that I had reached the point where "surgical therapy would be of most benefit."

Therefore, I had a retrospigmoid vestibular nerve section as described by my surgeon, Dr. Michael E. Glasswork III, in his booklet, *A Discussion of Meniere's Disease*. In a personal letter to me, he wrote the following brief description of this surgery: "This operation is performed via a suboccipital craniectomy. The dura is incised in a T-fashion, and the cerebellum is retracted out of the way to provide visualization. The vestibulocochlear nerve and facial nerve are then identified. The vestibular nerve is sectioned preserving the cochlear and facial nerves."

After surgery, I had no balance nerve on my right side. I shall always have Meniere's disease, but the attacks have been eliminated, thank God. I have *never* had a severe attack since surgery, and never shall I forget a very happy experience after leaving the hospital. I was standing on the second floor of my niece's home in Nashville. Looking outside at the top of the trees, I exclaimed, "I can see the leaves on the trees . . . and there are houses on the hill." The disease had put me in the shoes of one with impaired vision; now the joy of the reverse—I could see!

I later learned that I do have fuzzy vision as explained in a document put out by the Vestibular Disorders Association, Portland, Oregon. Dr. Charlotte L. Shupert wrote,

Vestibular disorders cause two kinds of problems with vision:

1. Inability to see clearly while moving. Examples: Objects appear to move around when you drive, walk, or move your head. . . .
2. Sensitivity to certain kinds of visual scenes. Examples: Dizziness increases when you look at . . . "busy" patterns on wallpaper, etc., or rows of similar objects in stores. . . .

Unfortunately, the visual system is easily tricked by patterns or moving objects into believing that the body is moving when it is not. The resulting confusion among the senses causes dizziness and nausea.

While the surgery caused me to make an adjustment to an imbalance problem, I know that one fall saved my life. I fell backwards off my exercise bicycle, sustaining a brain concussion. Cerebral aneurysm tests revealed a cerebral aneurysm and my life took another sudden turn. I had been a walking "time bomb." After numerous consultations, the decision was left to me: "watch it," or have surgery. That was a traumatic experience and entailed many decisions. Everything was left to me, but I was not walking alone. "Even when walking through the dark valley of death I will not be afraid, for you are close beside me, guarding, guiding all the way" (Ps. 23:4 TLB).

I could not *control* the situation, but I could *take charge* of my response to the circumstances, with the Lord beside me, giving me wisdom to make the right decisions.

Before giving consent for surgery, I updated my will with an entirely different outlook on life. I prayed that nothing would be overlooked, as I didn't expect to return to my home on this earth after surgery. With the aneurysm in the memory section of my brain, I was also told that if I survived the surgery, I might become like a vegetable—merely existing. Therefore, with understanding and compassion, my lawyer answered my questions on certain legal matters that concerned me. I obtained a living will and a power of attorney. My decisions were clear to me before surgery, and I know that those decisions were what the Lord wanted me to do.

There were two verses that gave me great comfort during those stressful weeks. They were "Be strong and of good courage; be not be afraid, neither be thou dismayed: for the Lord thy God is with thee whithersoever thou goest" (Josh. 1:9 KJV). And the other was "trust the Lord completely; don't ever trust yourself. In everything you do, put God first, and he will direct you and crown your efforts with success" (Prov. 3:5b–6 TLB).

I prepared for surgery emotionally, mentally, and spiritually. My life was in His hands and I had perfect peace as I was wheeled into the operating room.

When I awakened after surgery, I heard a friend calling my name. Opening my eyes momentarily, I saw two men standing beside my bed. One I knew, and later I learned the other one was the head surgeon. I closed my heavy eyes, wondering why they were there. I was amazed, and even disappointed; I had expected to awake in heaven.

When the neurosurgeon came to my room with his assistants, he told me, "I put you back the best way I could, but I could *not* put you back the way you were made." At times I have an indescribable feeling in my head that reminds me of his words!

As I lay in the hospital with a swollen, bruised face and a bandaged head, I could only think of my Creator, who had given wisdom to man to perform such a surgery. The following scripture ran through my mind: "I will praise You, for I am fearfully and wonderfully made; Marvelous are Your works, And that my soul knows very well" (Ps. 139:14 NKJV).

How can I help but say "to God be the glory for the great things he has done!" He is keeping me alive today by a tiny little clip on an artery deep within my brain.

If I could write songs of praise, they would flow from me. But someday I will be in the great multitude shouting, "Alleluia! For the Lord God Omnipotent reigns!" (Rev. 19:6b NKJV).

Four months after the aneurysm, I had my second back surgery. The fall that led to the discovery of my aneurysm did severe damage to my already painful back and arthritic spine. My sciatica and osteoarthritis had worsened after that last surgery. The pain was unbearable!

Later when I was at the Mayo Clinic, a rheumatologist sent me to the pain clinic, where it was recommended that I have nerve blocks, either there or by a specialist in Mississippi. Furthermore, I was urged to stay twenty-eight days longer in the pain management clinic program at St. Mary's Hospital. It was impossible for me to stay any longer.

Upon returning home, I discussed the recommendations with my physician. I had three nerve blocks, but *without* relief. Nerves in that large area, from the waist down, had been cut too much from surgeries for any effective results from nerve blocks. Anti-inflammatory medications, cortisone, and whatever else my doctors prescribed, had too many side effects. It was like a vicious cycle from physical and aquatic therapy to pain management consultations—through the entire medical gamut.

I was literally exhausted, but with no relief.

After discussing with my physician the painful efforts of making physical preparations for appointments, driving some thirty miles roundtrip only to return home with the same amount of pain as when I had left, the choices were clear, and my decision was made.

I would do at home all I had learned under his supervision. Thus, I took charge of a daily program to care for my physical problems. I am the only one who feels and listens to my body's signals, and I feel that I know my body better than anyone else. It tells me when I should stop, not that I always stop at the first signal. I can be stubborn, maybe unreasonable, but I just accepted another challenge—to take charge of my pain.

Life is exciting, and there is so much to do. I would not have a pity-party about the universal plague called pain. I was determined to do everything possible to help myself endure as long as I had strength to work with my problems and also manage the aging process.

Isn't it exciting to live in such a wonderful country as America with so many opportunities and freedom to do as we wish? I want to grasp every opportunity within my limitations, as long as it is physically possible. I become perplexed to hear someone say, "I am bored," or "I don't have anything to do." For me, I don't have enough time to do the things I want to do each day.

I decided I would invest my energies in a busy health-improvement program at home. I had had physical therapy and medical consultations from the East Coast to the West Coast, from the South to the North, and I wanted to put my learning experiences into a consistent, workable plan for me. I began working on a twenty-four-hour awareness schedule, trying to avoid stressful situations and to do everything with enthusiasm—as I did when I was holding a job.

A positive attitude, I knew, was important to help me take charge of my chronic health problems. Therefore, it was necessary to *tune out* negative thoughts or remarks.

Some treatments had neither been pleasant nor helpful, but I knew the ones that had helped me. If the medical authorities had agreed on some simple treatments that even I could do, then I would do those on a regular basis. This is where therapy at home became an essential part of helping improve my everyday battles. I have tried to combine a little common sense with professional medical advice. This doesn't mean that I haven't attended the arthritis support group or arthritis aquatic class, but my daily home life has changed. Therefore, from the time I awaken each morning until bedtime, I am mindful of therapeutic procedures that are beneficial for me.

My Home Therapy Plan

When possible, I do a stretching exercise in bed as a warm-up. Have you watched your dog or cat take a long leisurely stretch after a night's sleep or sometimes after taking a nap? They have a built-in instinct. It feels good to them. Good example for us human beings!

During my stretching exercise, I stretch my legs, arms, fingers, and my entire body. A person may be able to do more or less than others. Some exercise is excellent for the circulatory system also, and it gives me a good start for the day.

While doing my stretching exercise, I also do my breathing exercise. Of course this procedure must be modified when I am having any asthma problem. Normally, I have been instructed to breathe in slowly through my nose and blow out through my mouth. When done correctly, the lips are pursed as if to whistle.

Then there is the slow-rising motion. When getting out of bed, I sit on the side of the bed for a few moments instead of immediately standing. (If one has hypertension, Meniere's disease, or vestibular disorders, this is especially important to avoid falling.) I have learned not to jump out of bed as I used to do. My therapist's advice on the slow-rising motion is valuable as we grow older.

Another breathing exercise I find extremely beneficial is done in a warm or hot tub. (My respiratory therapist agrees.) I cover my face with a wet, warm cloth and do my breathing exercise. When I inhale, I hold my breath and let the moist, warm air stay in my lungs as long as I can hold my breath. I exhale slowly and repeat several times. This also opens my sinuses and nasal passages. This moist heat treatment is excellent for colds, sore throats, bronchitis, and other respiratory problems. It is important to follow your therapist's or your doctor's advice. I *emphasize* that what I have found is good for me *may or may not* be good for others. Each person *must* follow the therapist's or doctor's instructions on an individual basis.

Dressing as soon as possible is a part of therapy. I feel that lying around, or roaming around the house in nightclothes, can be demoralizing, and even detrimental. (Also, because of its weight, my TENS unit is held better by day clothing.)

The TENS (Transcutaneous Electrical Nerve Stimulation) device gives electrical pulses to stimulate the nerves in painful areas, which sometimes blocks the severity of the pain. Some people may be annoyed by the low-intensity electrical signals, which cause a tingling sensation at the site of the electrode. Or some may not want to be bothered with the time element involved in using this small, battery-operated stimulator that has electrodes which are taped to the skin. The electrodes are connected to wires, called leads, which are inserted into the unit. The electrical signals pass through the lead wires to the electrodes. Inadvertently, I have hit the intensity controls and felt an uncomfortable, strong stimulation, which is frightening until the intensity is lowered to a tolerable level. As soon as the battery goes dead, I know immediately because the pain noticeably returns.

My only complaint is occasional skin irritation at the electrode sites, which is my own fault for using the same site when placing a new electrode. Since I have used a TENS unit off and on for a twenty-year period, I have developed a workable scheme through trial and error. (A TENS unit must be prescribed by your physician.)

Dressing upon arising, I immediately connect my TENS unit, which also helps with morning stiffness, muscle spasms, and some arthritic pain. My TENS has two output jacks, so I can use four electrodes, two in the lumbar area, and two in the cervical area. Actually, there are times I would like to have two TENS units . . .

I do wear loose clothing to hide the appearance of the TENS, which measures $2^{1}/_{2}$ inches by $3^{1}/_{2}$ inches.

Masking the appearance of pain is also important to me. My first step is masking my feelings with makeup, which serves as a good morale booster. Splashing cold water on my face before applying makeup is invigorating. If I am staying around the house, I apply light makeup, which is enough to lift my spirits because I feel and look better.

My second step in masking is my *tone of voice* when talking over the telephone. Before answering the telephone, I take a deep breath and think of something pleasant. Sometimes this does mask my feelings. When the call is too long for my body's endurance, the pain may eventually reveal itself.

My third masking attempt is in my telephone *response* to the question: "How are you today?" I could say, "Well, thanks for asking; how are you?" If I say "fine," then I would be lying. If I don't want to discuss how I really am, I may reply, "Oh, I'm hanging in there; how are you?" Sometimes, I find that *avoiding a direct answer* works by saying, "Well, hi! How are you?" A similar remark works just as well. For example, "Well, how nice of you to ask; how are you?" If I have been thinking of this person, I'll reply, "I've been thinking of you; how are you?"

The fourth masking effort is making a comment after someone says, "You look great!" or "You look as if you have never been sick a day in your life . . ." I agree that this is one of the hardest masking tasks. But I have found saying, "Thanks. You have made my day," or some similar compliment works better than any other remark I may voice.

My Nutritional Therapy

Realizing that water is vital for my body, I drink plenty of fluids throughout the day, most times as much as 80 ounces or more. I drink two glasses of water with medication (Fosamax) before breakfast, usually while I am preparing my orange juice and bowl of shredded wheat with plenty of milk.

My cereal has no salt. It has been extremely hard to learn to eat without salt, but I have learned from necessity.

Years ago, after my heart catheterization, a dietitian recommended to me a cookbook that the American Heart Association published called, *Cooking without Your Salt Shaker*. Interestingly, my Meniere's disease doctor's staff member recommended the same book, because for several health reasons, I should have no sodium. However, I have learned how to prepare my foods without using a guide but with common sense. I learned that herbs and spices can replace salt.

Isn't it disturbing to see some people do just the opposite from what they know is best for their health? Life is short and full of aches and pains. Why neglect doing what we know is best?

Dietitians, physicians, and all nutritionists tell us to eat plenty of fiber, which I get in my cereal. I also eat fresh vegetables, fruits, and grains. A balanced diet is part of my therapy. The saying "You are what you eat" holds much truth for me. As we grow older, diet becomes even more important. When we are placed on a special diet, we should understand the prescribed diet and then follow it. For example, I am allergic to corn, products containing corn, and even fumes from the steam of boiling corn on the cob or popping corn. Understanding my prescribed diet has been important to the development of tolerance, and the annoying symptoms have gradually disappeared in the months I have followed my doctor's computerized diet.

Special diets, whether for allergy, diabetes, hypertension, heart—or diets that restrict sodium intake and eliminate caffeine—require learning to read labels on all prepared items, whether canned, frozen, or baked goods. This makes for an interesting education, essential to our well-being. Determination, self-control, and the desire to adjust are well worth the effort. Living within our limitations can make life more comfortable for us and those around us. I want to cooperate with those who know what is best to help improve my health because it may mean less pain. Whether it is a balanced diet, or special diet, it is one that has been personalized to deal with my health problems.

My diet also contains foods that have a natural source of calcium, which helps prevent or slow down osteoporosis. It may be that I am more aware of this because this disease turned a beautiful friend of mine into a stooped, deformed old woman who experienced several broken bones during years of suffering. This is typical of osteoporosis, which mainly affects women. But men are *not* totally exempt. How sad to see sufferers of osteoporosis; I wonder why medical help was not given during their crucial years. Of course, smoking, alcohol, lack of exercise and estrogen, a diet lacking in calcium (and I am sure other factors) contribute to this disease that causes deformities and weakness in bones.

My physician recommended antacids that are calcium-rich and sodium-free. I am now on Fosamax and take one faithfully every morning with at least two or more glasses of water. Another preventive medication for osteoporosis I take, is estrogen. My physician had a specialist regulate my dosage. This helps slow down the loss of bone mass and may help keep calcium in the bones. There are risks with estrogen, so only doctors should recommend this individually.

Other Therapy

I am forever thankful that I have a physician who, on my regular office visits, checks my medications. He is always trying to find the best therapy for me. Therefore, I consult with him whenever another doctor recommends a change in medications or treatment, and I await his approval. I feel it is wise that my family physician agrees with all facets of my health program; hence, I keep in touch with him and have confidence that he knows what he is doing for my health's sake.

Medications are always explained by my physician, including the purpose of a drug and if there may be any side effects.

First, medication instructions should be thoroughly understood. If written instructions on the bottle are not clear, I ask the pharmacist to explain everything that I need to know about the medication. Usually, a printout on the medication is given along with the prescribed drug.

Next, I put the medication in a safe, accessible, and "in-sight" place, but not where they are accessible to children if I know they will be in my home.

I arrange my medications in a row by my sink (or wherever convenient). Then after taking each of my medications each morning, *I turn the bottles upside down.* This signifies that I have had each medication as prescribed. If two of the medications are taken at noon, then after taking them, I move those two bottles over a few inches (in a new row) in an *upside-down position.* If the same two medications are taken in the evening, then I move the bottles *back* to their original morning position.

Ready to begin my next day's schedule, I turn all bottles upright again. If for any reason there is doubt in my mind as to whether or not I have taken a medication, I do not take that dosage. Thus, this prevents taking a double dosage, which could be more harmful than not taking the drug. Some people prefer using the plastic containers easily marked for daily and weekly dosage, which may be safer if forgetfulness is a problem.

Heat therapy is primary in my treatment for severe back and joint pain. *Moist* heat pads are good for my entire back. But warm, or hot water—as hot as my body and heart permit—has proved to be the most beneficial for me. In a tub, I can submerge my entire body and get quicker relief than I can from any other temporary therapy. Alternating hot and cold treatments have been used successfully on my back by physical therapists, and an ice pack was used to freeze certain small areas. When my pain was localized, I have also used ice packs at home. However, arthritic and diabetic patients are always given medical instructions regarding using hot or cold treatments, or both, with the warnings that go with each.

Massage therapy, recommended by my physician, has proved one of my best treatments for arthritis, sciatica, muscle spasms, fibromyalgia, headaches, and sinusitis. A good benefit of this therapy is the increase of blood flow, thus helping any circulatory problem. Also, a therapist should be able to pinpoint all sore areas and use heated oil to help ease any muscle pain. When massage therapy is used, I feel it should be done on a regular schedule to get the maximum benefit. Furthermore, a massage should be administered by a therapist who is trained to work with *all* medical problems. I am grateful that my physician referred me to the therapist I have.

Exercise may be painful for chronic pain patients, but some type of exercise program is always suggested by one's physician or therapist. I started with a five-minute program and gradually worked up to my maximum tolerance, which varies. My body has taught me to learn the difference between normal and excessive exercise pain. Swimming and exercising in a heated pool, with the temperature no lower than 90 degrees, has been my most beneficial exercise. My sauna used to be of great help until that had to be eliminated.

I use 3-pound bell bars as weights for my arm exercises, and I do arm exercises while using my stationary bicycle and stretch at the same time I am bicycling. Exercising in a hot-water tub is good for my legs, arms, fingers, and back, and a good time to do the pelvic tilt. Throughout the years, I have received various exercise manuals with the exercises suggested as best for me. Aerobics may be good for some chronic pain patients, but not for me.

We all react differently to exercise programs, and I believe our body is the judge. Medical advice is important in this area. Sometimes it is necessary to cutback on certain exercises; I let my body and common sense be my guide. However, my physician agrees that jumping, bouncing, and strenuous exercise are not for me.

Walking is an excellent exercise for those who can do it. I have a toy poodle who goes on a sit-down strike if I don't walk her when we go to the mailbox. Her sister tags along, enjoying every new smell and attention-getter, especially the squirrels. I wonder if I am walking them or if they are walking me. I would be running if they had their way.

Pet therapy is high on my list of the best therapeutic agents I can recommend to anyone. I believe that my pets are an integral part of my daily therapy—and a happy diversion. My first pet was a beautiful little brown poodle who helped fill the void when I was left alone after my dad's struggle with Parkinson's disease and other painful problems. That was over thirty years ago, and I hope I shall always have a little poodle in my life as long as I live. Through these many years, my pets have brought me laughter, joy, and love. In my book, *Always a Mimi—A True Poodle Story*, I wrote:

> As children growing up in the wide-open spaces of rural Mississippi, my brothers and I were permitted to have many pets. However, several years later as a teenager in Washington, DC, I was deprived of the joy of having a pet. Then one day while shopping, I found a souvenir plaque, which recalled some childhood memories. In the center was an eye-catching picture of two dogs, and surrounding the striking picture were these words: Our friends—Those who know us but still love us. I purchased the keepsake, not knowing at the time that the inscription would become a reality in the form of three beautiful, communicative, and loving toy poodles.

I was privileged to see a person's life transformed through the love of my poodles. Her grief after the loss and shock of her husband's suicide was so great that she was institutionalized for therapy. On her visits home, she came to know and love my little poodles. Spending time with them, she was gradually able to overcome the shock of her grief and was able to be discharged permanently from the institution. Those three special poodles were Mama Mimi, and her offspring, Gorgeous Black Fifi and Little Brown Gigi (her image).

Mimi, Fifi, and Gigi

Anyone with such loving pets can be helped through many painful situations. My veterinarian, Dr. A.G. Harrell, has written an outstanding article, "Pets Can Have Soothing Effects." With his permission, I quote some excerpts:

> Man has coexisted on this earth with animals since creation. Dogs guarded the camps against wild animals in prehistoric times; now they watch and listen, alerting us to burglars or unusual activity outside our homes.
>
> Veterinarians and pet owners have long recognized and known, subconsciously perhaps, that pets also contribute to human mental health and emotional well-being. More than half the families in this nation keep pets, recognizing their value as friends to the old, the lonely, the physically infirm, and the mentally ill; their worth in teaching children tenderness, responsibility, and respect for living creatures. Companionship is felt to be the major benefit of the human-animal bond. In addition to companionship, psychiatrists feel pets provide the additional functions of something to care for, something to keep one busy, something to touch, and a relaxing focus of attention, exercise, and safety.

Dr. Harrell wrote in his article about some companion animal benefits studies I feel is worth emphasizing: "Study of ninety-two heart patients found those who owned pets had a significantly higher chance of surviving one year longer than those who did not own a pet."

Dr. Harrell concluded, "For many people, lives are enriched, emotional well-being improved; a need for loving and caring is fulfilled (whether we will admit it or not) all because of what we feel toward our pet."

I feel strongly that "Our little pets are made to love and to be loved," as I wrote in *Always a Mimi—A True Poodle Story*. My poodles, through many years, have proved my truest friends. They know when I am in pain; their concern shows on their faces. Their loving, soothing presence brings a joy in spite of pain. They are happiest, and show it, when they are with me, and their actions prove their love for me. They are my ears, my eyes, my shadow, and my heart. Only the presence of my pets can give the love, joy, companionship, and quiet comfort in my times of greatest pain, whatever kind of pain it may be. Thank God for His wonderfully made little creatures. In His wisdom, He gave to mankind one of the greatest therapeutic agents for suffering people. Those of us in pain, who take advantage of our kind, loving, caring, comforting, beautiful pets, will have in return, our best friends on this earth. Nothing grieves me more than to see a pet suffer from an illness; no grief has been greater than the loss of one of these precious God-given little creatures.

Any human being who purposefully mistreats a pet, or any animal, reveals his inner character and the condition of his heart. The wicked ways of man may be evidenced by the way he treats his pet.

The incredible, torturous reports of cruelty to animals will never be recorded in my writings, because I find such horrendous acts are too repulsive. It has been noted by medical authorities and social workers that children who perform cruel acts on animals are often the persons who maim, or even murder, later in their lives. Therefore, any such violent acts should be reported at once to the proper authorities, not only for the benefit of the injured animal, but also for the much-needed emotional and mental help for the human individual.

I believe that God's Word gives the best proverbial insight concerning how He regards anyone who harms creatures that God Himself made. God said in Genesis 1:26, 28b that He gave man "dominion over" or (as I have combined several translations) made him the "master" of every living creature that moves on the earth. So God puts us in charge of the animals. And I believe that His word in Proverbs 12:10 gives the best description of how God looks upon man by the way these God-made creatures are treated: "A righteous man regards the life of his animal (is concerned for the welfare of his animals TLB), But the tender mercies of the wicked are cruel" (NKJV).

I feel that what a man is really like is shown by the way he treats his pets or animals, and I substantiate my belief on this proverbial statement. According to this proverb by one of the wisest and wealthiest kings of Israel in his day, even the wicked, or cruel man, doesn't know how to be kind, or even gentle, with an animal. Proverbs 12:10b states clearly my feeling "but even the kindness of godless men is cruel" (TLB). Thus, animal cruelty is a revelation of man's heart. Man's harsh acts to animals cause pain to all who love them. Many children and adults have had broken hearts because of senseless acts of cruelty to their pets. Therefore, I can *not* remain silent!

Therapy for the Mind

Laughter is an "ice-breaker." When something happens to break the walls of bitterness, loneliness, tension, stress, depression, or unbearable pain, laughter is the best medicine. And my pets have ways of bringing smiles and laughter to me by some of their actions.

Relaxation of body, mind, and spirit is a vital part of my therapy at home. I cannot meet each day until I simply turn off the whole world and remember Psalm 46:10: "Be still, and know that I am God" (NKJV). He created my being, and I cannot function properly without spending time with my Creator, who is Lord of my life. This may mean turning on my answering machine or simply taking the phone off the hook, but I do what is necessary to meet my need for quietness and meditation.

At my age, I have confirmed the words of Isaiah, the Hebrew prophet that "in quietness and confidence shall be shall be your strength" (Isa. 30:15*b* NKJV). And also:

> Have you not known? Have you not heard? The everlasting God, the Lord, the Creator of the ends of the earth, Neither faints nor is weary. *There* is no searching of His understanding. He gives power to the weak, And to *those who have* no might He increases strength. Even the youths shall faint and be weary, And the young men shall utterly fall, But those who wait on the Lord Shall renew *their* strength; They shall mount up with wings like eagles, . . .

. . . They shall run and not be weary, They shall walk and not faint. (Isa. 40:28–31 NKJV)

How exhilarating! Those uplifting, powerful words in Isaiah have proved true to me many, many times. Within my heart, I have embedded those encouraging words, which are like the beautiful, joyful sound of a bird singing in the early morning hours.

This is my secret of strength and *I know* that He is my strength and not just the source of my strength. As a teenager, I chose Philippians 4:13 as my life verse: "I can do all things through Christ who strengthens me" (NKJV). So I know from experience that He is my strength at all times. I sing with David in Psalm 27:1*b* that "The Lord is the strength of my life" (NKJV).

Thus, I have that inner peace and joy, and I proclaim with Nehemiah in verse 8:10*b*: ". . . the joy of the Lord is your strength" (NKJV). And I say the joy of the Lord is *my* strength! This truth keeps me going. He fills my thoughts and mind with His thoughts. He gives me a song that keeps me happy!

Worrying doesn't change problems, but creates stress. And we all know that stress can lead to many illnesses—even stroke or heart attack. Therefore, I don't worry. Why should I? My mother used to worry about anything. At times she would say to me, "Why aren't you worrying about . . . ?" My reply would be, "Why should I? I can't do anything by worrying but make myself sick and unhappy." And many times she did make herself sick by worrying.

I always think of the following verses taken from Matthew 6:26–30, 34:

> Look at the birds! They don't worry about what to eat—they don't need to sow or reap or store up food—for your heavenly Father feeds them. And you are far more valuable to him than they are. Will all your worries add a single moment to your life? And why worry about your clothes? Look at the field lilies! They don't worry about theirs. Yet King Solomon in all his glory was not clothed as beautifully as they. And if God cares so wonderfully for flowers that are here today and gone tomorrow, won't he more surely care for you? . . . So don't be anxious about tomorrow. God will take care of your tomorrow too. (TLB)

Music is part of my relaxation. Tuned to my favorite local Moody Bible station, my radio plays throughout my home from the time I arise until bedtime. Its soothing music is relaxing and uplifting, and it's excellent therapy to join in singing one of my favorite songs. Thus, I've learned that singing relaxes my body and helps relieve any tension. No one but my poodles hears me, and singing brings joy to my soul; that is what counts!

Beside my bed is a cassette player, surrounded with all kinds of tapes. Whether I am resting or ready to turn in for the night, the sound of music or New Testament tapes is the best "medicine" for me.

Reading is another resource that takes my mind away from painful problems. My home is filled with books and magazines for excellent reading moments. I am extremely interested in comparing different translations of the Bible; I can get involved in hours of study, instead of merely reading.

Nothing is more exciting to me than preparing for a Bible study as I wait on the Holy Spirit to give me something new or fresh during that intercessory time with Him.

Prayer and quiet meditation is just talking to the Lord who is ever-present. I remember the old hymn "Take your burdens to the Lord, and leave them there." Who else can take our burdens? Or as someone remarked when we were discussing advertising my poodle book, "Who cares?" There is a Person who cares about everything concerning my life—and the lives of all of us—and that is the Lord God.

I can lie flat on my back, or in any position, and pray either silently or out loud, and I *know* He hears me. What a comfort, especially in times of pain!

I have other ways to relax too, and one relaxation technique was taught to me by a California physician. As I lay on his examining table, he told me to stretch out and tighten my entire body into rigidity until he counted to five. Then he said, "Relax." Beginning with my toes, I was instructed to concentrate on relaxing each toe slowly, gradually moving from my toes to my feet, legs, thighs, on up to my head. Several times he had me repeat this sequence so I could do it at home. *It works.*

This same physician also lectured me for about twenty minutes on suicide. I later learned that he had just lost a doctor-friend who had taken his own life, leaving a shocked, grieving family and friends. My physician pointed out that suicide is actually *murder*, which is against God's commandment "You shall not murder" (Exod. 20:13 NIV). He pointed out that it is a selfish act of destruction, not only to one's self, but also to the devastated loved ones left behind. He reiterated, "God has a purpose for each life; that purpose is never known when one takes his own life, which is rejecting God's plan and will."

His friend had been in severe pain for a long time. He felt his friend had probably had a feeling of utter despair, not being able to endure suffering any longer. So adding to the remembrance of his words, my advice is: Never let the thought enter your mind; it is not of God. Suicide is a forever act! It cannot be undone! Stop and think; *never* act in haste but seek help if you have the feeling of not being able to endure your pain.

Isolation is the expression I use when I know that it is essential for me to withdraw from people and noise and to get a complete rest during severe painful bouts. It has been hard to learn to say "no." But what others think is not my problem. Dealing with chronic pain is not understood by everyone, even though they may think they do.

I need not be defensive. Some people may be confused or even doubtful, because chronic pain patients don't look or act as if they are suffering. Then I am happy that I don't reveal suffering, which is exactly what I try to *mask.* Thoughtless remarks don't bother me anymore. If I don't take care of myself, no one else will. Therefore, I am in charge of self-help, which may allow me to participate in activities at some later time.

Kathryn Hagen has Ehlers-Danlos syndrome, osteoarthritis, and cardiac problems. She worked for fifteen years as a registered nurse in mental health and critical-care areas and now writes for a variety of publications. Her article, "Coping with the Invisible," appeared in *Arthritis Today* magazine. With her permission, I quote some of her words from this illuminating article, which is based on her personal experience:

> My joints weren't "hot" or "red." My blood tests were all normal. Yet the pain, fatigue, and weakness I experienced were real. Since childhood, I'd lived with these invisible symptoms— but without a name for what was wrong. Many people didn't believe me or, at least, didn't seem to. It's understandable; there was nothing for them to see. Sometimes I even wondered whether the problem was all in my head.

She continued, using some strong words that help me in coping with similar situations: "Often it's not the crude comments of insensitive strangers that hurt us most—it's the reactions of family and friends, the people we assume we can count on when times are tough."

I appreciate the *Arthritis Today* magazine for publishing such articles as Kathryn Hagen's. They help me in coping with the invisible and the remarks of people, whether direct or indirect.

For those of us who fall in the category of not being able to do the many things we want to do, it is painful to miss special trips, shopping sprees, church functions, and other interesting events.

Pacing my activities requires getting my health priorities in order; thereby, I try to live as normal a life as possible within my individual circumstances and limitations. Learning the importance of taking control of my pain, and learning to say no when necessary, means I can do more than I used to. I don't push beyond my limitations as often now; hence, I am not as tense and frustrated by trying to please everyone—and then paying for it later by having to take a day off for complete rest. In fact, I would not be able to write this book on pain had I not learned to take control of my circumstances!

Setting goals, sometimes more than I could possibly accomplish, has been one of my trademarks. Each day I plan things to be done. In earlier years, I made a time schedule, then was frustrated when I didn't reach my goals for that day.

It took a friend to face me with my problem. I was surprised when she met me in our college hall one day and confronted me about striving to accomplish more than I could possibly do in one day, with the consequent stress and disappointment, which she could see. She helped me more than she will ever know!

I was shaken by the fact that I was punishing my body by pushing to meet the time I had allotted for each goal. I actually lived by my watch, but today I set goals more realistically. I plan what I would like to do each day, but if it doesn't get achieved, I don't push or fret. I accept the fact that tomorrow is another day. I find that some of those tomorrows have grown into months, and in some cases, years. Nevertheless, I don't run out of enjoyable things to do. This change in my way of thinking and living has caused a less stressful life. Some days I still realize I have put myself into a demanding position of planning more than my body can do.

I think of the eagle flying high above the clouds in seemingly tranquil contentment. Then I slow down, take life easy, and *do what I can, when I can.* I take charge of every moment to avoid creating more pain. This is exactly what I am teaching myself every day in taking control of pain: Use the eagle as a motivational reminder to be content with every hour of every day. I do my best within my limitations and rest in the fact that God is in control of my life.

In my bedroom is a beautiful beveled glass plaque with a picture of an eagle flying high above the clouds. Underneath the clouds is an inscription of Isaiah 40:31a: "But they that wait upon the Lord shall renew their strength. They shall mount up with wings like eagles." (TLB).

I placed this plaque in a prominent position as my cue to think of living above the clouds, not dwelling on things below with all the pain and heartache. When I see this eagle plaque first thing in the morning and all during the day, it is my reminder that I *can* soar freely and serenely above the clouds in my life.

What a boost! I stand tall, hold my head high, and take charge of my efforts to live like the eagle, flying above all problems. It's a great symbol to me of God's sovereignty!

A beautiful, majestic bird has been used in the word of God to illustrate the power of God available to me when I learn to simply *wait* on Him. He lifts me up as if I am "on eagle's wings," as He said to Moses to remind the Israelites in Exodus 19:4. The result: I can "mount up with wings like eagles." This thought is a great motivation; I accept it in helping me to take control of pain!

In summary, my therapy-at-home program, which I do throughout my daily activities, consist of:

1. A positive attitude
2. Stretching exercises
3. Breathing exercise
4. The slow-rising motion
5. Moist heat, warm water
6. Dressing first thing in the morning
7. TENS unit in constant use during waking hours
8. Masking of pain

9. Drinking water and plenty of other fluids
10. Plenty of fiber
11. Adhering to a balanced or special diet
12. Proper medication instructions
13. Heat therapy
14. Massage therapy
15. Exercise
16. Pet therapy
17. Laughter
18. Relaxation of body, mind, and spirit
19. Decline to waste time by worrying
20. Music and singing
21. Reading for enjoyment
22. Prayer and meditation
23. Relaxation technique
24. Suicide thoughts dispelled
25. Isolation when necessary
26. In charge of self-help
27. Coping with the invisible
28. Setting goals
29. My motivational eagle plague
30. Accept that God is in control
31. "God's phone number" (to follow)

If each person who reads this chapter and this book could realize my heart's desire and prayer is to help others endure their problems and trials, then I know that one of God's promises, which I have claimed throughout this writing, has been fulfilled once again for me.

God's Telephone Number
The promise in Jeremiah 33:3 has been called "God's telephone number" and is illustrated by a gift from one of my dearest friends who has shared her painful experience in one of the first chapters of this book. She knew that Jeremiah 33:3 is one of the Bible verses I have claimed throughout the years. Over my kitchen telephone

on the wall is a framed treasure that shows a telephone with the words, "GOD'S PHONE NUMBER," and centered on the pictured telephone is a circle with that scripture reference. Around the outline of the telephone is the verse, "Call to me and I will answer you and tell you great and unsearchable things you do not know" (Jer. 33:3 NIV). Across the bottom of the picture are the large bold instructions: TOLL FREE—DIAL DIRECT—24 HOURS. In order to take control of my pain, I just *call* on Him, knowing that He will answer me and show me great and mighty things that I know not. He has in the past, He is doing so now, and I know that He will continue to do so in the future.

Postscript

In retrospect, I am overwhelmed as I've watched the way God touched the hearts of those who responded to my request for sharing their most painful experiences. It is my prayer that their suffering and endurance can be used to help others and at the same time glorify Him.

As I have reviewed the stories that appear in this book, I am amazed to see how God was in control of every response. The experiences are so diverse that I do not believe any human being could have organized such an assemblage. My response is a heart filled with praise and awe: To God be the glory for the things He has done—and for the things He will do as we continue to wait on Him.

What an awesome God!

Appendix

~⑪⑪⊙

Alzheimer's Disease Research
 A program of the American Health Assistance Foundation
 15825 Shady Grove Rd., Suite 140
 Rockville, MD 20850
 800-437-AHAF
 fx: 301-258-9454

American Diabetes Association
 1660 Duke St.
 Alexandria, VA 22314
 800-232-3472

American Humane Association
 (Animal Protection Division)
 63 Inverness Dr. E
 Englewood, CO 80112-5117
 303-792-9900
 fx: 303-792-5333

Arthritis Foundation, Inc.
 800-933-3032

Arthritis Foundation National Office
  1314 Spring St. NW
  Atlanta, GA 30309
  Automated Information Line: 800-283-7800

Arthritis Today (magazine)

Association for Children with Down Syndrome
  2616 Martin Ave.
  Bellmore, NY 11710
  516-221-4700
  fx: 516-221-4311

Ben Lippen Schools
  PO Box 3999
  Columbia, SC 29230-3999

Centers of Disease Control and Prevention, (CDC)
Dept. of Health & Human Services,
Statistics & Epidemiology Branch
  4770 Buford Hwy.
  Atlanta, GA 30341-3724
  404-488-7083

CHILDHELP USA
  (1345 El Centro Ave.)
  PO Box 630
  Hollywood, CA 90028
  213-465-4016
  fx: 213-466-4432

Columbia International University
  7435 Monticello Rd.
  Columbia, SC 29230-3122
  803-754-4100
  fx: 803-786-4209

Coral Ridge Ministries
  5555 N. Federal Hwy.
  Fort Lauderdale, FL 33308
  305-771-8840
  fx: 305-771-2952

EAR Foundation
  1811 Patterson St.
  Nashville, TN 37203
  800-545-HEAR
  615-329-7807
  fx: 615-329-7935

Indianapolis Project, Inc.
  One RCA Dome, Suite 110
  Indianapolis, IN 46225
  317-639-4773
  fx: 317-639-5273

Jungle Aviation & Radio Service, Inc. (JAARS)
  PO Box 348
  Waxhaw, NC 28173
  704-843-6000

Medic Alert
  2323 Colorado Ave.
  Turlock, CA 95280
  800-825-3785

Meniere's Network
  1811 Patterson
  Nashville, TN 37206
  615-329-7809
  800-545-4327

Mission Aviation Fellowship
PO Box 3202
Redlands, CA 92373
909-794-1151
fx: 909-794-3016

National Safety Council
1121 Spring Lake Dr.
Itasca, IL 60142-3201
708-285-1121

National Spinal Cord Injury Statistical Center
1717 Sixth Ave. S, Rm. 544
Birmingham, AL 35233-7330
205-934-3450

Parkinson's Disease Foundation, Inc.,
William Black Medical Research Bldg.,
Columbia-Presbyterian Medical Center
650 W. 168th St.
New York, NY 10032
800-457-6676
212-923-4700

Pet Partners: Delta Society
321 Burnett Ave. S, Third Floor
Renton, WA 98055-2569
206-226-7357
fx: 206-235-1076

United Cerebral Palsy Association, Inc.
1522 K St. NW, Suite 1112
Washington, DC 2000
202-842-1266
800-ISA-5UCP

United Network for Organ Sharing (UNOS)
  (Donor information)
  1100 Boulders Pkwy., Suite 500
  Richmond, VA 23225-8770
  24 hours: 800-355-SHARE
  fx: 804-330-8517

Vestibular Disorders Association
  PO Box 4467
  Portland, OR 97208-4467
  503-229-7705
  800-837-8438
  fx: 503-229-8064

Wycliffe Bible Translators
  PO Box 2727
  Huntington, CA 92647
  714-969-4600
  fx: 503-229-8064

To order additional copies of

Living above Pain

send $12.99 plus $3.95 shipping and handling to

Books, Etc.
PO Box 1406
Mukilteo, WA 98275

or have your credit card ready and call

(800) 917-BOOK

But they that WAIT
upon the LORD
shall RENEW
their STRENGTH,
they shall mount UP
with wings as EAGLES.
Isaiah 40:31